THE PLAY OF

The Secret
DIARY
of
ADRIAN MOLE
aged 13¾

SUE TOWNSEND

Songs by Ken Howard and Alan Blaikley
Notes and questions by Alison Jenkins

Heinemann Educational Publishers
Halley Court, Jordan Hill, Oxford OX2 8EJ
Part of Harcourt Education

Heinemann is the registered trademark of Harcourt Education Limited

First published in Great Britain as a Methuen Paperback original in 1985
by Methuen London Ltd,
First published in the *Heinemann Plays* series by Heinemann Educational
in 1992.

13

A catalogue record for this book is available from the British Library on
request.

10 - digit ISBN: 0 435232 83 5
13 - digit ISBN: 978 0 435232 83 2

Cover design by Keith Pointing (cover picture features Gian Samarco as
Adrian Mole in the Thames Television production).

Designed by Jeffrey White Creative Associates.

Typeset by Taurus Graphics, Abingdon, Oxon.

Printed in China by CTPS

Contents

Contents

Introduction

The play, and adaptation of Sue Townsend's book of the same name, follows the events in the life of a young teenager. It looks at the real, everyday problems and anxieties facing young people in a lively, humorous way, which will make enjoyable reading, whether in small groups or as a class.

Ideas for follow-up work can be found at the end of the play. The first section, *Keeping Track*, comprises straightforward questions on the text. These can be completed orally, or in note-form, as the students read through the play.

Suggestions for a more detailed look at some of the issues raised in the play follow in the section called *Explorations*. Finally, a bibliography gives details of Sue Townsend's other plays and novels and a short glossary right at the end of the book provides a useful reference for allusions in the text and for potentially difficult words.

The play may also usefully be used alongside the book of *The Secret Diary of Adrian Mole Aged 13 ¾*, to look at the changes Sue Townsend made to the original in adapting it as a stage play. This can form the basis for exploring the different conventions and requirements of the two genres.

There are a number of songs in the play. If it is being read in class, these can, of course, simply be read out. If it is being performed, music is provided at the end of the book. The author's note which follows also has a lot of useful tips about staging. *The Play of the Secret Diary of Adrian Mole Aged 13 ¾* was created for the Phoenix Arts, Leicester, where it received its first production in September 1984. It was subsequently staged at Wyndham's Theatre, London, in December 1984.

Alison Jenkins

Author's Note

If you are thinking of staging this play I send my very best wishes to you. I think it's quite a tricky play to stage. It is episodic and therefore flits about from scene to scene, and it demands a great deal from the young man who is to play Adrian Mole; a lot of lines to learn and moves to remember.

Graham Watkins, the director, and I were lucky in finding a superb young actor, Simon Schatzberger, to play the first Adrian Mole.

The play is set in Leicester and I think works best with East Midlands or Northern accents.

The Mole family are upwardly-mobile working-class; that is, they don't keep ferrets in the bath, and George Mole has bought his own house. The play had its first performance at the Phoenix Arts Centre in Leicester and translated very well (complete with Leicester accents) to the West End stage at Wyndham's Theatre.

Staging

The original production had an inspired setting. Anthony Dean designed a huge cut out dolls' house with a kitchen, hall and stairs, and living room downstairs; and a bathroom, Adrian's bedroom and his parents' bedroom upstairs. Gauzes and lighting effects were used to focus on specific rooms. Other scenes were played out in front of the house with the minimum of sets and furniture.

The play could work equally well with the simplest sets possible, or even none at all

The Dog

The Mole dog is an important character. In the first production three puppets were used. A sitting-up dog, a lying-down, floppy dog and a show-stopping walking dog on wheels. The three puppets became unnaturally life-like in Simon's hands. However, if three puppets are beyond your budget, then try for at least one. If that's impossible, then go to the RSPCA and start training a real dog.

Voice overs

Adrian's diary extracts are often used to link scenes, and should be pre-recorded. This gives the young actor a chance to breathe and reminds us that what we are seeing on stage has just been, or is about to be, written into a 'Secret Diary'.

Music

Ken Howard and Alan Blaikley have written some lovely songs. In Leicester the musical accompaniment was kept to the Scrooge-like minimum of two electric pianos and drums. In the West End it blossomed out into two electric pianos, drums and guitar. But should Joe Loss be your brother-in-law, then by all means ask him to play for you and arrange the band parts.

Style

The actors shouldn't have to break their necks for laughs providing they go for the truth of what they are saying. Audiences are not thick and are capable of recognising and even laughing at a joke without having it pushed down their throats. Go for a good pace and try not to let it flag. And whether you are performing in the play or reading it at home, I hope you enjoy it.

Very Best Wishes,

Sue Townsend

Act One

Scene One

Music: The Mole Overture

At the end of the Overture, Adrian comes to the front of the stage. He talks directly to the audience.

Adrian This is just my luck! I've come all the way from Leicester to hear a lecture about George Eliot only to be thwarted at the last minute because the American lecturer missed Concorde. What am I going to do now? I'm doing George Eliot for my English Literature project. I've written him loads of letters, but he hasn't replied to one. Still, with a bit of luck I might be able to mingle with a few intellectuals in the foyer.

He looks round at the audience.

There's loads here tonight. But I bet *they* don't live an ordinary life like me. No, they're lucky, they go home to book-lined studies and intellectual families.
Perhaps when my diary is discovered people will understand the torment of being a thirteen and three quarter-year old intellectual. Until then I'll just have to put up with the charade that is my family life.
I bet Malcolm Muggeridge's family didn't carry on like mine did on New Year's Eve.

The lights go up to show the New Year's Eve party.

Grandma and Mrs Lucas are sitting on the sofa.

Pauline and Mr Lucas are dancing together.

George is drinking from a can of lager.

Adrian joins Nigel at centre stage.

Everyone, including Adrian, is wearing a party hat.

Nigel I shall be glad to get home, I've been bored out of me skull all night.

Adrian	I warned you not to come, Nigel. You should have stayed at home with Andy Stewart … Do you want your coat?
Nigel	Yeah, I want to split, man.
Adrian	Why are you talking like an American?
Nigel	Because I'm fed up with being English. I'm searching for a new identity.
Adrian	You're never satisfied, Nigel.
Nigel	So was that all you got for Christmas, a digital radio alarm clock?
Adrian	Yes, that and the new *Beano* annual.
Nigel	What's it like this year?
Adrian	It's a bit too childish now, for my taste.

Suggestive dancing from Mr Lucas and Pauline.

They go into the kitchen still dancing. Grandma watches disapprovingly.

Nigel	Is your mum drunk or does she always dance like that?
Adrian	She's drunk, I'm afraid.
Nigel	It's embarrassing watching adults trying to dance isn't it?
Adrian	It's enough to make you sick.

Grandma stands up.

Grandma	George! Coat!

George fetches Grandma's coat and helps her on with it.

Grandma speaks to Mrs Lucas:

Grandma	It was very nice of you to talk to me. I enjoyed our chat about double glazing. Goodnight.
Mrs Lucas	Goodnight.

Mrs Lucas starts tidying up.

Grandma	I shan't bother saying goodnight to Pauline.

She raises her voice:

I know she didn't want me at the party. Night, Adrian!

Adrian   Night, Grandma!

George and Grandma go off.

In the kitchen Mr Lucas has his hands on Pauline's shoulders, talking straight to her face. He is saying how long he has fancied her.

Nigel   You haven't seen my new bike yet, have you?

Adrian   No.

Nigel   It was made by a craftsman in Nottingham

Adrian   Mine was made by my dad in our back yard.

Nigel   Honestly, Adrian, your consumer durables are a disgrace. Where's your mum?

Mrs Lucas   She's in the kitchen, I shouldn't go in. I think she's busy.

Nigel   Right.

Nigel shouts:

Thank you for the party, Mrs Mole. I shall remember it for the rest of my life!

Pauline is in the kitchen:

'Night, Nigel pet!

Pauline and Mr Lucas separate.

Nigel   You can come round tomorrow and have a go on my Steve Davis snooker table if you like.

Adrian   I'm half way through a poem. I'm hoping to finish it tomorrow.

Nigel   Suit yourself, Moley. 'Night Mrs Lucas.

He leaves.

Mrs Lucas   'Night, Nigel. Take care walking home. Don't get yourself mugged.

Pause. She looks at Adrian.

You look tired, love, why don't you go to bed?

Adrian   I've got to take the dog for a walk first. It's no wonder I'm short for my age.

Adrian takes the walking dog out from under the stairs cupboard and goes off as Mr Lucas comes out of the kitchen.

Mr Lucas speaks to Mrs Lucas:

Right, you ready?

Mrs Lucas   Have you said 'Goodnight' to Pauline?

Mr Lucas   Yes, yes, come on. I want my bed.

Mrs Lucas   No you don't. You want Pauline's bed.

Mr Lucas   What's brought this on?

Mrs Lucas   I'm not blind, deaf and dumb. You're going to have an affair with her, aren't you?

Mr Lucas   I hardly know the woman.

Mr Lucas   Well, who *are* you going to have an affair with then? You didn't buy yourself three pairs of Pierre Cardin underpants for nothing!

Mr Lucas   Look you agreed that we'd have an open marriage didn't you?

Mrs Lucas   Yes – open. But not *wide* open. Not the woman next door.

Mr Lucas   So it's a matter of geography now, is it?

Mrs Lucas   Look, I know that you need other women. It's a sort of hobby with you, isn't it? Like other men go potholing or sky-diving. But *they* don't do it in their own backyards, do they?

Mr Lucas   She's wasted on George. My God, he must be the most boring man in Leicester.

Mrs Lucas   Well, I'm going home to get some sleep. I'm knocking the kitchen wall down tomorrow.

She starts to leave.

Mr Lucas raises his voice:

Look I'm sorry. It's not my fault I was allocated too many hormones is it?

Mrs Lucas   There's no need to shout!

Mr Lucas   There's every need. We've got another bloody year to get through.

They go off.

Pauline comes out of the kitchen singing 'My Way'. She doesn't know the words. George comes in and watches her for a moment.

George Come on, duck, time for bed.

Pauline George I've got to tell you. It's my New Year's Resolution. (*Pause.*) George, nobody wears flared trousers nowadays. (*Pause.*) Nobody.

George looks at his flares.

George Jim Reeves does.

Pauline But Jim Reeves is dead, George.

George Jim Reeves will never die.

They go upstairs singing. George sings 'Your Hair of Gold' Pauline sings 'My Way'.

Adrian comes in, carrying the dog. It still has the lead around its neck.

Adrian The stupid thing only got to the end of the road before it collapsed. I've a good mind to report my father to the RSPCA. He shouldn't have made the dog drink all that cherry brandy at the party last night.

He goes to the foot of the stairs and listens to Pauline and George singing and arguing in the bedroom.

There is a chance that my parents could be alcoholics. This time next year, I could be in a children's home.

He speaks to the dog:

You'd better sleep with me tonight.

Adrian goes upstairs with the dog. The lights go on in his bedroom. He puts the dog on the bed, and writes in his diary.

Voice over.

Adrian Just my luck. It's the first day of the New Year and I've got a spot on my chin where everyone can see it. It's my mother's fault for not knowing about vitamins.

The lights go down in the bedrooms.

Scene Two

The lights are on in the living-room. George Mole is sitting in the untidy living-room fixing his model of the 'Marie Celeste.'

Pauline enters looking rough.

Pauline George, I'm dying.

She flops into a chair.

George You deserve to be, Pauline. You drank enough Pernod to demolish the Thames Barrier.

Pauline Well it's only once a year.

George And I don't like the way you were dancing either.

Pauline I know I'm a bit out of practice but I didn't think I was that bad.

George You were dancing in a suggestive, not to say wanton, manner. Mr Lucas got all of a doodah, I was watching him.

Pauline We were doing the *tango* George, we weren't Morris dancing.

Pauline gets up and starts to tidy up.

Is Adrian up?

Lights go up in Adrian's room to show Adrian trying to force an aspirin down the dog's throat.

George He's trying to give the dog an aspirin.

Pauline Why, what's up with it?

George It's got a hangover.

Adrian enters.

Pauline You were the life and soul of the party again, weren't you Adrian? How many times have I told you? If you're not enjoying yourself, then *pretend* that you are. *I* have to do it at your lousy school concerts.

George Have you been at my glue?

Adrian No.

George Well, it's not where I left it. You're sure you didn't take it up to your room for a quick snort?

Pauline As if he would.

George That's what Jack at work said about his lad. Next thing Jack knows, his lad's been arrested for hijacking a Bostik lorry. That's teenagers for you.

Pauline But Adrian's not a normal teenager, George.

Adrian Yes I am!

Pauline Don't be silly, of course you're not. You're polite to me and your dad, you keep your room tidy and you don't play your stereo system at full decibels.

Adrian I haven't got a stereo system, that's why!

George We're not made of money, Adrian.

Adrian I wasn't asking for one.

Pauline What's that on your chin?

Adrian A spot.

Pauline shudders.

Pauline Uuugggh!

Adrian It's because I don't get enough Vitamin C.

Pauline Go and buy an orange then.

George Nobody talk to me. I'm rigging the sails.

Pauline Did you make any New Year's resolutions, petal?

George shouts back:

George I said don't talk to me!

Pauline shouts:

Pauline I'm talking to Adrian!

Adrian Yes, I made ten.

Pauline Oh, what were they?

Adrian	Oh, you know, helping the poor, stuff like that.
George	I'm glad to hear it. You can help me by turning your bedroom light off a bit earlier. And you left your heated rollers on again, Pauline.
Pauline	You're getting obsessive about us using electricity. You know that, don't you? You begrudge us every therm we consume.

Adrian goes out and sits on the stairs. He listens carefully to the conversation.

George is gradually exploding.

George	Electricity is money, Pauline! Hard earned money! And until you and him start bringing some money into this house, I shall be as obsessive as I like. I shall stand and watch the little wheel go round, I shall build a bloody shrine around the meter cupboard, I shall ...

Pauline stands up.

Pauline	Right that does it! I'm getting a job!

George stands up.

George	No wife of mine goes to work!
Pauline	How many wives have you got?
George	Why can't you be happy to stay at home? You've got it made. A little light housework in the morning. A quiet stroll around the shops in the afternoon. Bit of telly in the evening.
Pauline	You have just described a day in the life of a convalescent snail! You sexist pig!
George	Here we go, here we go. She's read two chapters of *The Female*-bloody-*Eunuch* and she's already surburbia's answer to Greasy Greer.
Pauline	It's Germaine.
George	Germane to what?
Pauline	Let's not row, George. Not on the first day of the New Year. Adrian will hear.

George replies bitterly:

George	Adrian, it's always Adrian! He's a disappointment to me, Pauline, I don't mind admitting.
Pauline	Just think, fourteen years ago he wasn't even here.
George	And then when he was here you wanted to send him back.
Pauline	Yes. He was an ugly baby though, wasn't he? ... I mean I know he's our son but ...
George	Grotesque's the word. I've seen better looking gargoyles.

George and Pauline laugh. Adrian is upset and angry. He puts his raincoat on.

Pauline	I used to dread people looking into the pram. I had to keep the cat net up permanently.

Adrian comes forward.

The music to 'The House Where I Live' underplays the following dialogue.

Adrian	Bye!
Pauline	Where are you going?
Adrian	Out. To buy an orange.

George and Pauline go upstairs.

The House Where I Live

Adrian sings:

She doesn't cook me my meals,
Doesn't know how it feels
To be hungry and young:
And he doesn't budge from his chair,
Doesn't care if I'm here – or there!

Yes, this is my family seat,
Eighteen Every Street
It's the house where I live.

They ought to care if I smoke,
Ask if I'm sniffing coke,
Disapprove of my friends:

I could be in some gangster's pay
Or be wasting away, day by day!

While they sit there sunk in their gloom
I could meet with my doom
In the house where I live.

No cheerful fire in our hearth,
Badedas in our bath,
Aerosol in the loo:
Who sees if we've run out of tea?
Or the dog's done a pee? – It's me!

Yes, here in its bleak monochrome
Is my own broken home,
It's the house where I live,
Yes, this is my own broken home,
It's the house where I live.

During the song, George and Pauline are seen in the house in separate rooms. By the end of the song, they are in bed together, in their bedroom. At the end of the song, Adrian takes off his coat and puts a lurex apron on.

Scene Three

Adrian My parents have got the flu. This is just my luck! It was cough! cough! cough! last night. If it wasn't one, it was the other. You'd think they'd show some consideration. I've been up and down the stairs day and night with trays of food and drink.

Mr and Mrs Lucas enter. Mr Lucas is carrying a bouquet of flowers.

Mr Lucas Ah, young Adrian. As you see I bear a floral gift for the invalid.

Mrs Lucas He means he's brought your mother some flowers (*Pause.*) Are you all right?

Adrian No, I'm a bit worn out to tell you the truth and another worry is that the dog's left home.

Mr Lucas Surely that's a cause for celebration?

Mrs Lucas Bimbo!

Adrian Oh I know it shouldn't have jumped on my father's model ship and got tangled up in the rigging, but there was no need for my father to threaten to have it put down. (*Pause.*) Shall *I* give her the flowers or do you want to see her?

Mrs Lucas He wants to see her.

Mr Lucas goes towards the stairs.

Mr Lucas You go for lurex in a big way do you, Adrian? ...

He laughs.

Adrian I bought it for my mother for Christmas, but I haven't seen her wear it yet.

He takes the apron off.

My mother told me to warn her if any visitors came ... to give her time to put her make-up on.

Adrian goes upstairs to his parents' bedroom.

Mr Lucas Why are you still tagging on? Haven't you got a drain to clean or something?

Mr Lucas speaks to Mrs Lucas.

They sit down to wait. Pause.

Mrs Lucas speaks casually to her husband:

Mrs Lucas I was lying in bed last night trying to work out ways to kill you.

Mr Lucas I thought you were reading.

Mrs Lucas No. (*Pause.*) I decided on a seaside mishap.

Mr Lucas Go on.

Mrs Lucas explains eagerly:

Mrs Lucas You know how you make me bury you up to your neck in cool sand when we're on the beach?

Mr Lucas Yes.

Mrs Lucas Well, I thought I'd just carry on and bury your ugly head as well.

She smiles.

Mr Lucas Very nice.

Mrs Lucas	I'd bring your body back to England, you wouldn't like to be buried in Benidorm, would you?
	Mr Lucas is shocked.
Mr Lucas	No.
Mrs Lucas	But then I decided against it.
Mr Lucas	I'm very pleased to hear it.
Mrs Lucas	No. I can't wait for the summer. Why don't we have a winter holiday instead? We could go skiing and I could chuck you over a precipice.
Mr Lucas	Wouldn't it be simpler to get a divorce?
Mrs Lucas	Oh it would be *simpler* but not half as satisfying. Look, can't you find yourself a young, single girl? The wine bars are full of them.
Mr Lucas	I want Pauline.
Mrs Lucas	And Adrian. He's part of the package.
Mr Lucas	I don't mind. I've always wanted a son and Adrian's past the stage of screaming in the night.
Mrs Lucas	If we'd had children it wouldn't have made any difference. We've got nothing in common.
	She goes off.
	I'm a woman and you're a man!
	Mr Lucas prepares himself to see Pauline. He combs his hair and sprays breath freshener into his mouth.
	The lights go up in Pauline's bedroom to show Pauline sitting up in bed applying lipstick. George is also in the bed. Adrian is standing next to the bed.
Adrian	Shall I tell him you're ready?
	Pauline sprays perfume on to herself and into the air.
Pauline	Just a minute. I must get rid of the smell of the sick-room.

George   You can tell him I'm asleep.

George pulls the sheet over his head.

Adrian shouts downstairs:

Adrian   She's ready!

George   What's *he* coming round for? I didn't visit him when he had haemorrhoids, did I? I left him in peace.

Pauline   He's only being neighbourly, George. Put the sheet back over your head.

Mr Lucas walks upstairs. George reads the Daily Express *under the sheets. Mr Lucas enters the bedroom. Mr Lucas and Pauline stare Adrian out.*

Adrian goes to his room to write his diary. Mr Lucas sits on Pauline's side of the bed. He hands her the flowers. He kisses his fingers and transfers the kiss to Pauline's lips. Pauline is conscious of George awake under the sheets.

Mr Lucas, how kind of you! They're beautifully unnatural! They must have cost a fortune!

Mr Lucas   No sweat, Mrs Mole. I know a bloke at Interflora.

Pauline   George will love them when he wakes up.

Mr Lucas   Been asleep long, has he?

Pauline   No, he's just dropped off.

Pauline says 'He's awake' in dumb show.

Mr Lucas   I won't stay long, I just wanted to see you …

He takes Pauline's hand and presses it to his mouth, almost eats it.

…and George.

Pauline   Well, I'll tell George you came. He'll be sorry to have missed you.

She grabs Mr Lucas's hand and kisses it.

How's Mrs Lucas?

Mr Lucas   She's well, she sends her love.

Mr Lucas kisses Pauline's neck and shoulders. Pauline tries to wrench his head away. During the following dialogue, Mr Lucas and Pauline kiss, cuddle, touch etc.

Pauline   I do admire your wife, the way she installed your gas central heating single-handed! I'm so helpless myself. I have to get George to change the light bulbs.

Mr Lucas   You're a very feminine woman, Mrs Mole. You don't want to be messing about with light bulbs. I'm sure you've got other skills at your fingertips. Artistic skills …

Pauline   Oh I have, I have, but I haven't used them for so long …

George turns over in bed. Mr Lucas and Pauline fly apart. Mr Lucas picks up The Female Eunuch.

Mr Lucas   Bedside reading eh?

He reads.

The Female Eunuch. Yes I've heard of that. I read a book once …

Pauline   Did you? What was it called?

Mr Lucas   It was called *I Want You.*

Pauline becomes frantic.

Pauline   I don't think I'm familiar with that title. *The Female Eunuch* is *very good*; it's making me re-think a lot about my role as a woman. Fixing my own light bulbs for instance.

George grunts.

Pauline   He's talking in his sleep.

Mr Lucas   Well, there'll be murder done if I don't get home to the wife. So, I'll love you and leave you, Mrs Mole. Any idea when you'll be back in circulation?

Pauline   It will be very, very soon.

They blow each other kisses. Mr Lucas goes.

George   I've never heard such a load of silly slobber in the whole of my life.

Pauline   Oh stuff some Vick up your nose and shut up!

Scene Four

Adrian comes downstairs wearing his school uniform and carrying his briefcase. He comes downstage. The lights go up on a school wall and netball post.

Adrian When Mr Lucas went, my father had an argument with my mother and made her cry. My father is still in a bad mood. This means he is feeling better. I made my mother a cup of tea without her asking, this made her cry as well. You just can't please some people!

Pandora enters bouncing a netball. She practises shooting at the net.

There is a new girl at our school. Her name is Pandora but she likes to be called 'Box'. Don't ask me why. I might fall in love with her. It's time I fell in love. After all, I am thirteen and three quarters years old.

Adrian stands staring at Pandora.

Pandora Do you mind? You're ruining my concentration.

Adrian Sorry. I was just admiring the way you handled the ball.

Pandora Netball is a ridiculous game. So one gets the stupid ball in the stupid net. Who cares?

Adrian Well you're very good at it.

Pandora I'm good at most things.

Adrian I'm no good at sport.

Pandora How boring for you.

Adrian Oh, I don't mind. I'm more the intellectual sort.

Pandora turns to look at Adrian.

Pandora Are you clever as well as being intellectual?

Adrian No. I'm about average really.

Pandora You poor thing. What *do* you excel in?

Adrian I write poetry.

Pandora	Juvenile stuff I suppose.
Adrian	Well I *am* a juvenile.
Pandora	Boring isn't it? Hanging around waiting to grow up. I mean what's the point? One's no longer a child, so why go through this dreary half and half stage?
Adrian	You used to go to a posh school didn't you?
Pandora	Yes, but then Mummy and Daddy got a conscience about it. They're both socialists, so they threw me into the comprehensive system.
Adrian	Do you like it?
Pandora	One school is very much like another, isn't it? All that shouting and bullying. Teachers are the same everywhere. Fascists.
Adrian	What, like Hitler, you mean?
Pandora	Oh yes. Well, perhaps not *quite* as bad as him. But they do rather think that they're the master race, don't they?
Adrian	You go to the 'Off the Streets' Youth Club, don't you?
Pandora	Yes, there's rather a banal disco on tonight, isn't there?
	Adrian stares.
Pandora	What are you staring at?
Adrian	Your eyes. They're the same colour as our dog's.
Pandora	What sort of dog is it?
Adrian	It's a mongrel.
Pandora	Gee thanks!
	Nigel enters wearing whatever is current teenage high fashion.
Nigel	Hi, Box!
	Pandora is pleased.
Pandora	Oh hello, Nigel. You look brillo pad.
Nigel	Thanks.

Adrian	Where's your uniform?
Nigel	In the cloakroom. I'm going to town to buy some gear to wear to the disco tonight.
Adrian	Why can't you wear your uniform in town?
Nigel	I'd sooner die.

Pandora speaks to Adrian:

Pandora Somebody might see him.

Nigel speaks to Pandora:

Nigel	Are you having a relationship at the moment?
Pandora	No, actually I'm just recovering from one.
Nigel	Like me. I've just broken one off. She was three-timing me.
Pandora	Still it gives one the chance to draw breath doesn't it? Have a look round, see what's available.
Nigel	Well, I'm available.
Pandora	Well, we'll have to see what fate has in store for us, won't we?

She goes off watched by Nigel and Adrian.

Adrian	Oh God, she's beautiful! She's got hair like treacle.
Nigel	What, sticky?
Adrian	No! It's the colour of golden syrup.
Nigel	You're in love with her, aren't you?
Adrian	Yes.

Nigel puts his arm round Adrian.

Nigel	Well forget it, Moley. You're not in the same division. She's a class bird. She won't *look* at a guy unless he's got at least a hundred quid's worth on his back and you've got to have the right brand names – the right labels.
Adrian	OK. If you're the expert on clothes tell me what intellectuals wear.
Nigel	Why?

Adrian Because I think I'm turning into one. It must be all the worry.

Nigel When did you turn?

Adrian Last night. I saw Malcolm Muggeridge on the telly and I understood nearly every word.

Nigel Well, write to *him* and ask him what to wear.

Adrian I don't know where he lives do I?

Nigel Well write to him care of the British Museum then, that's where all the intellectuals hang out isn't it? See you.

Nigel goes off.

Adrian is contemptuous of Nigel.

Adrian The British Museum! Intellectuals don't waste their time looking at old statues and stuff, they're too busy writing poems and appearing on BBC book programmes. Yes! I'll write to Mr Muggeridge care of the BBC. I'd better enclose a stamped addressed envelope because Mr Muggeridge *is* an old aged pensioner and probably can't afford a first class stamp. I'll soon be an expert on old aged pensioners. I've joined a group at school called The Good Samaritans. We go round doing good in the community and stuff. The old people were shared out at break today. I got an old man called Bert Baxter. He's eighty-nine so I don't suppose I'll have him for long.

Scene Five

At the youth club disco. Loud music. Dim lights. Nigel pogos onto the stage. He is dressed as a weekend punk. He dances for a a while in a madly exhibitionist style. The music is turned down in volume. Nigel reacts angrily.

Nigel Hey! Where's the sounds?

Adrian enters dressed in shirt, sweater, tie and

school trousers.

Adrian   That's better, it was hurting my ears. I asked Rick Lemon to turn it down.

Nigel   Haven't you been to a disco before, Mole?

Adrian   No.

Nigel   Thought not. You look like Frank Bough. Go and stand in the corner. I'm ashamed to be seen with you. Don"t you care what you look like.

Adrian   No. I don't. (*Pause.*) You look dead stupid. Doesn't your mother mind you being a punk at weekends?

Nigel   No. Not so long as I wear my string vest under my bondage T-shirt.

Adrian   You're not a proper punk, are you? I thought proper punks had safety pins in their ears.

Nigel   They do. I forgot to put mine in.

Pandora enters.

Pandora   Oh, it's Adrian Mole. In the half light I thought it was an old Crumblie.

Adrian   Crumblie?

Pandora   Somebody over twenty-five.

Adrian   You look very nice from what I can see. Is it always dark at discos?

Nigel speaks to Pandora:

Nigel   It's his first time.

Pandora laughs.

Pandora   Incredible! Never been to a disco before?

Adrian   No. and I don't think I'll bother again.

Nigel speaks to Pandora:

Nigel   I came out without putting my safety pin in my ear. So I'm about to do it now. You can watch if you like.

He takes a safety pin from his T-shirt.

Pandora   Oh you are brave – stupid, but brave.

Adrian watches, horrified, as Nigel inserts the safety pin.

Pandora Well done!

Nigel Oh, it's killing me! Get it out!

Adrian It's your own fault for showing off.

He gives Nigel a tissue.

Nigel I'm bleeding. Look – blood! It's pouring! I'm going to die!

Pandora It *is* gushing out, rather.

Nigel. Take me to the hospital. Get an ambulance!

Pandora comforts Nigel who is now close to fainting. They go off to loud disco music. Adrian comes to the front of the stage. He talks to the audience.

Adrian My father had to take Nigel to the hospital in our car. Nigel's parents haven't got a car because his father's got a steel plate in his head and isn't allowed to drive and his mother is only four feet eleven inches tall so she can't reach the pedals. It's not surprising Nigel has turned out bad really, with a maniac and a midget for parents.

Scene six

Adrian Today was the most terrible day of my life: I've got fifteen spots on my shoulders, my father is in a bad mood – he thinks his big-end is going. Pandora is going out with Nigel, but, worst of all, Bert Baxter is not a nice old age pensioner!

The lights go up to show Bert Baxter sitting half-undressed in a television chair. Empty beer bottles are under the chair, also an enormous jar of beetroot. A dog's bowl is beside the chair. An Alsatian dog barks loudly offstage.

Bert speaks fiercely:

Bert Who's there?

Adrian is half in the door.

Adrian sounds desperate:

Adrian Can I come in, please? I think your dog's trying to bite me.

Bert Bite yer! 'Ell 'ave yer bleddy leg off. He's a pure thoroughbred, radged-up Alsatian, ain't yer Sabre?

Sabre answers with a bark.

Quiet, sir!

Sabre is instantly quiet.

Who are you?

Adrian squeezes in.

Adrian I'm Adrian Mole from Neil Armstrong Comprehensive School.

Bert You got me out of bed.

Adrian Sorry, I thought you'd be up.

Bert Why?

Adrian It's the afternoon!

Bert What's that got to do with ought? A man of my age needs his sleep.

He sticks a Woodbine in his mouth.

Got a light?

Adrian No. I don't smoke.

Bert is shocked.

Bert Don't smoke! A lad of your age! You should be ashamed of yourself!

Sabre goes crazy behind the door.

Bert roars at him:

Bert Quiet, sir!

He speaks to Adrian.

He's hungry. You wouldn't have a spare tin of dog food on you, would you?

Adrian No. (*Pause.*) Mr Baxter, the school sent you a

letter about me. It was to warn you that I'd be coming round.

Bert Why, what are you – a burglar?

Adrian No. I'm a Good Samaritan. I go round doing good in the community.

Bert What for?

A long pause.

Adrian I miss maths.

Bert So you've come round here to do me some good, have you?

Adrian Yes, is there anything you'd like me to do.

Bert Yes, bugger off!

Adrian Then could you sign my paper to prove that I've been?

Bert No. I never sign nothin', that way they can't get you.

Adrian Who?

Bert The Government.

Adrian But it's only for the school.

Bert Schools is run by governments, ain't they? Don't you know ought?

Bert slaps his legs.

Come on me old beauties! Here, you can go and get me shoppin' in for me. Now concentrate because I'm going to tell you what I want and I 'ate repeatin' myself. Twenty Woodies.

Adrian Woodies?

Bert Woodbines, lad. Concentrate. A jar of beetroot, a tin of Chum, three bottles of brown ale and the *Morning Star*.

Adrian Is the *Morning Star* a newspaper?

Bert What's up wi' you, lad? Are you backward? The *Morning Star* is the only newspaper worth readin'. The others are owned by capitalist runnin' dog lackeys.

Adrian   So – Twenty Woodies. A jar of beetroot. A tin of Chum. Three bottles of brown ale. The *Morning Star*. Could I have the money, please?

Bert   Tell 'em to put it on my account. On account of how I've got no money left.

Bert laughs and goes off.

Sinister music as Barry Kent enters.

Kent   Mole! You weren't at school this morning, Mole.

He sprays 'B.K. OK?' on a wall. Adrian tries to leave without being seen. Barry Kent has his back turned.

Kent   Stay where you are, Mole!
Where you bin, Mole – Skivin'?

Adrian stands perfectly still with his back turned to Kent.

Adrian   No. I've been out, being a Good Samaritan.

Adrian starts to go off.

Kent   I said, stay where you are.

Kent puts the full stops on his graffiti.

Adrian   I've got to go. I've got a test on the Norwegian Leather Industry ...

Kent   Who gives a toss about the Norwegian Leather Industry?

Adrian   I do. I'm a bit of an expert. I expect to get full marks. Let me go.

Kent   I ain't touched you. You could go if you wanted to.

Adrian   You know I can't.

Kent approaches Adrian.

Kent   Give me twenty-five pence an' you can go freely on Her Majesty's footpaths.

Adrian   I haven't got twenty-five pence.

Kent   You got your dinner money, ain't you?

Adrian   I haven't. My dad pays by cheque since it went up to seventy pence a day.

Kent straightens Adrian's tie.

Kent   All you poofters have pocket money, don't you?
For helping your mummies with the washing
up?

Adrian   Mine goes straight into the Market Harborough
Building Society. All I get is sixteen pence a day
– for a Mars bar.

Kent   Oh dear, oh dear. Then you're in trouble, Mole
'coz I need twenty-five pence a day from you,
so's I can maintain my present life-style. You
seen the price of Doc Martens?

Kent twists Adrian's arm.

Adrian   You're hurting me, a bit.

Kent   Sorry, gotta do it. I ain't 'ad your advantages.

Kent continues hurting Adrian.

Adrian   Now you're hurting me a lot.

Sorry, Gotta Do It

*During this song Kent beats Adrian up and kicks
him in the goolies and generally humiliates him.*

Kent   Sorry, gotta do it, gotta do it,
Sorry, gotta do it,
Nothing personal – know what I mean?

What you need is my protection:
In return I take collection
Of a paltry pound or three – it
Makes good sense! Invest in me! Like

You're the client, I'm the banker:
I need finance, you're a wanker!
Things are as they ought to be, now
I've got you and you've got me – see?

Sorry, gotta do it, gotta do it,
Sorry, gotta do it,
Sorry, gotta do it, gotta do it, gotta do it:
Nothing personal – know what I mean?

Breathe a word and you'll regret it!
Think of squealing? Don't forget, it's
Me you'll have to answer to – and
In the end, I *will* get you! I'll

Have your little guts for garters,
Mash your face in – just for starters!
'Coz you know my golden rule is
No holds barred! Go for the goolies!

Sorry, gotta do it, gotta do it,
Sorry, gotta do it,
Sorry gotta do it, gotta do it, gotta do it:
Nothing personal – know what I mean?

The song ends with Kent standing triumphantly over Adrian who is crying.

Adrian   I've changed my mind. I will give you twenty-five pence a day after all. I'll get a paper round.

Kent   Well that's real decent of you, Mole. 'Ere have a tissue. I ain't heartless.

He throws Adrian a Kleenex and goes off. Adrian wipes his eyes, blows his nose, then stands and tidies himself up.

Adrian   Woke up next day with a pain in my goolies.

Scene Seven

Adrian picks up a newspaper sack. He sees Pandora crossing the stage wearing her riding hat and jodhpurs. He hides until she's gone. He looks at the papers he is to deliver to her house.

Adrian addresses the audience:

Adrian   Pandora lives at 69 Elm Tree Avenue. They have *The Guardian, Punch, Private Eye* and *New Society*. Pandora reads *Jackie* – the comic for girls; so she is not an intellectual like me. But I don't suppose Malcolm Muggeridge's wife is either.

Adrian crosses to the house, reading The

Guardian. *He stops at the threshold. He turns to the audience.*

It's full of spelling mistakes! It is disgusting when you think of how many people who can spell are out of work.

He goes upstairs to his bedroom and writes in his diary.

Voice over.

Pandora has got a little fat horse called Blossom. She feeds it and makes it jump over barrels every morning before school. She looked dead good in her riding stuff. Her chest was wobbling like mad. She will need to wear a bra soon.

The lights are up on Adrian's bedroom, and Pauline is in the bathroom cleaning the loo.

He speaks to the audience:

My mother came into my room this morning and started mumbling on about 'Adult relationships' and 'life being complicated' and how she must 'find herself'. She said she was fond of me. 'Fond'!!! and would hate to hurt me, and then she said that for some women marriage was like being in prison.

Pauline comes downstairs, puts her coat on.

Marriage is nothing like being in prison. Women are let out every day to go to the shops and quite a few go to work. I think my mother is being a bit melodramatic.

Pauline   Adrian, I'm off to my 'Women's Workshop on Assertiveness Training'. When your father comes home, tell him his dinner is in the freezer. (*Pause.*) At Sainsbury's.

Pauline leaves.

George Mole enters from work.

George   I'm home! (*Pause.*) Pauline, I'm home!

Silence.

George mimics Pauline.

Oh, hello George, how lovely to see you. How many storage heaters did you sell today? You sit down there in front of the telly, I'll bring your dinner in to you.

In his own voice:

What are we eating, Pauline?

He mimics Pauline:

Home-made steak and kidney pie, followed by spotted dick and custard!

In his own voice:

Yum yum! Come here, wife.

Adrian watches from the stairs.

George mimics Pauline:

Oh, George! Don't! The dinner will spoil! Oh, all right then …

In his own voice, bitterly:

Some bloody hope!

Adrian enters.

Where's your mother?

Adrian Gone to a women's workshop on assertiveness training.

George swears under his breath.

Adrian What *is* assertiveness training?

George God knows, but it sounds like bad news for me!

Adrian She's bought herself some of those overalls that painters and decorators wear.

George Was she wearing her high heels with it?

Adrian Yes.

George So there's still hope. Lipstick?

Adrian Yes, but it was that lip gloss stuff, not her usual orange.

George I knew it. Give her a fortnight and she'll be running around in monkey boots and a bristly hair cut. They've no right to interfere!

Adrian Who?

George Those bloody workshop types. They go around stirring women up telling them they're unhappy. (*small pause.*) Is there a boil-in-the-bag cod-in-butter sauce left in the freezer?

Adrian No, she hasn't been to Sainsbury's. She's been looking after Mr Lucas.

George What's up with him?

Adrian Mrs Lucas is leaving him. They're getting a divorce. Poor Mr Lucas is dead upset.

George Poor Mr Lucas could *be* dead for all I care.

Adrian You don't like him, do you?

George No.

Adrian Why? He's ever so nice and he really appreciates what Mum's doing for him.

George What *is* she doing for him?

Adrian She's comforting him for his tragic loss.

George swears under his breath.

George Is there any bacon in the house?

Adrian There's one slice.

George Where?

Adrian It's on the floor between the fridge and the cooker. It's been there for *three days* to my knowledge!

George It's bloody disgusting how she keeps this house lately, my socks have been in the Ali Baba basket for over a week!

Adrian I can't remember the last time she bothered to wash my PE kit. I have to do it myself or take it round to Grandma's.

George Poor kid. I'm very fond of your mother, Adrian, very very fond. But she's beginning to be a bit of a handful. Perhaps it's hormone trouble ...

George flings his shoes across the floor.

Switch the telly on, kid.

Television noise. Lights down. The TV closedown tone is heard. They sleep. Pauline enters. Lights up. She holds herself aggressively. Her voice is firm. She addresses George and Adrian who are still asleep. She is holding is large piece of card.

She addresses them loudly.

Pauline Right!

Adrian and George wake up.

The worm has turned! Things are going to be different around here! I am holding in my hand a chart; as you see, it is divided into three columns. Each column represents a member of this family. This is me, this is you, George, and this is Adrian.

Adrian What's all that writing under my name?

Pauline It is a list of household jobs. The first job on your list, Adrian, reads 'clean lavatory'. I know you think a little gang of fairies come out at night and fly round with the Harpic, but you are wrong. A *person* cleans the lavatory and until now that person has been me. But not any more.

She pins the chart up.

We start tomorrow!

Scene Eight

There is fast Mole music, then strobe light as Adrian runs around doing housework.

Voice over.

Adrian Cleaned toilet, washed basin and bath before doing my paper round. Came home, made breakfast, put washing in machine, went to school. Gave Barry Kent his menaces money, went to Bert Baxter's, waited for social worker who didn't come, had school dinner. Had domestic science – made apple crumble. Came home. Vacuumed hall, lounge and breakfast room. Peeled potatoes, chopped up cabbage. Cut finger, rinsed blood off cabbage. Put chops under grill, Looked in cookery book for a recipe for gravy. Made gravy. Strained lumps out with a colander. Set table, served dinner, washed up. Put burnt saucepans in to soak. Got washing out of machine; everything blue, including white underwear and handkerchiefs. Hung washing on clothes horse. Fed dog. Ironed PE kit. Cleaned shoes. Did homework. Took dog for a walk.

Adrian crosses the stage with the dog. He comes back on stage.

Adrian speaks to the audience:

Adrian Just my luck to have an assertive mother!

Lights up on Mr Lucas and Pauline in the kitchen.

Mr Lucas Paulie, Paulie. What we've got is something very rare and precious. We're like two sunbeams dancing on the ceiling of life. Together we could make a new sun, a new planet. We're cosmic, Pauline!

Pauline Stop it! I can't think straight when you talk like that.

Mr Lucas *I* can't think straight. I'm losing customers. I keep catching myself saying 'Oh why worry about the future?' It's not a healthy attitude for an insurance man to have. Don't think, Pauline. Just act. Come away with me!

Pauline I keep seeing the expression on Adrian's face the day his mouse died. He came home from junior school. I said: 'Hello pet, your mouse is dead.' He took it very badly.

Mr Lucas becomes sulky.

Mr Lucas Look, I'm not here to chat about dead pets, Pauline.

He turns away.

Pauline Oh come on, love! Since you moved next door,

I've had colour in my life; excitement. I couldn't wait to hang my washing out in the morning. 'Will he be in the garden?' I used to get through a Euro-sized packet of Ariel a week.

Mr Lucas   Did you? Did you really?

Pauline   Yes, not to mention the Comfort.

Mr Lucas   I'll be your comfort, and your joy, and your support. Your bodily lover, your spiritual helpmate, your companion in old age. I'll be your true, true love. Tell him tonight, Pauline, or I'm going to Beachy Head.

Pauline   Have you got relations there?

Mr Lucas   No, Paulie, pet. I shall chuck myself on to the rocks! I can't face life without my little sunbeam.

They are now just about to make love on the floor. Adrian comes downstairs and tries to get into the kitchen.

Adrian   Mum, are you in there?

Pauline   Yes, me and Mr Lucas are … mending the boiler. Can't it wait? Only I've got my hands full.

Adrian   Have I got any clean socks?

He shouts:

Hello, Mr Lucas!

Mr Lucas shouts back:

Mr Lucas   Hello, Adrian!

Pauline   I forgot to take them out of the washer. Sorry, sunbeam.

Adrian   I'll wear yesterday's again then,

He talks to himself:

Sunbeam?

There is a lighting change.

Scene Nine

Adrian speaks to the audience:

Adrian Went to school. Found it closed. What with all the worry I had forgotten that I am on holiday. I didn't want to go home, so I went to see Bert Baxter instead. I asked him if he would like to see a horse again. He said he would, so I took him to see Blossom. It took us ages to get there. Bert walks dead slow and he kept having to sit down on garden walls. Bert said that Blossom was not a horse, she was a girl pony. He kept patting her and saying 'Who's a beauty then, eh?'
Then we walked back to Bert's house. I went to the shops and bought a packet of Vesta chow mein and a butterscotch Instant Whip for our dinner, so Bert ate a decent meal for once. We watched 'Pebble Mill at One', then Bert showed me his old horse brushes.

Lights up on Bert with horse brushes. Adrian crosses to him.

Bert I turned into a communist before it became generally popular. I were one of the first. It happened on August 11th, 1910. At two o'clock. As you know, I were an ostler. That's doin' things with 'osses.
Well, one day, I'd got the 'osses brushed and gleamin'. It were a 'ot day, so I'd got a bit of a muck sweat on myself, when the lady of the house comes round the stables. She had her friend with her, pretty little thing in a blue dress, wi' a lace collar like a collection of snow flakes. Any road up, these ladies are wrinkling their little noses up on account of the smell of the 'oss shit. The lady of the house says: 'I say Baxter, is there nothing you can do about the smell in here?' I says: 'No Mum, not unless you can stop the 'osses shitting!' Well, you should have heard the carry on. You'd a' thought I'd said summat rude! I 'ad tuppence docked out o' me wages.

Then, later on that night, I seen the lady of the house feedin' chocolate eclairs to one of me best horses. Chocolate eclairs cost thruppence each – it were then I turned into a communist!

Adrian Why didn't you join the Labour Party, Bert?

Bert You know nought lad. Anyway, we were that poor, we never 'ad one.

The Bad Old Days

Bert sings to Adrian. At various points throughout the song, Bert and Adrian march and dance.

Bert When I was just your age, son,
When I was just a lad,
Things were far different then
I can tell you, my friend –
They were ten times as bad!
Had me no gilded youth, boy,
Lit by no sunshine rays –
We were fourteen in a hovel,
Takin' lessons how to grovel,
In the bad old days.

Lenin's my hero still, boy –
He was a man of steel:
If he came back today
His hair would turn grey
At the whole lousy deal!
Paid up and joined the Party,
Carried the big red flag:
We were comrades in an army,
Though they told us we were barmy,
In the bad old days.

They dance.

We toiled our youth away, boy–
No money, no thanks, no praise:
They say 'Where there's muck there's brass' –
I say 'Not on your bloomin' arse!'
They were bad old days.

Adrian and Bert go off.

Scene Ten

Lights go up on the Lucas garden. A trough of flowers and a gnome decorate the space. Mrs Lucas is uprooting trees and putting them into a wheelbarrow. She is wearing wellingtons and overalls. It is twilight.

Pauline Adrian said that you wanted to see me. (*Pause.*) Do you want any help with that bush?

Mrs Lucas No thanks, I'm stronger than I look. (*Pause.*) I'm leaving Derek tonight. I thought you ought to know.

Pauline Who's Derek?

Mrs Lucas That's your lover's name. He wasn't christened 'Bimbo'.

Pauline I can't think of him as being a Derek.

Mrs Lucas Does he still talk about sunbeams?

Pauline They've been mentioned in passing.

Mrs Lucas 'Two sunbeams dancing on the ceiling of life.' He knows how to get us going does Bimbo.

Pauline I love him.

Mrs Lucas I know, I did once.

Pauline I'm ever so sorry. I like you a lot. Oh – put that tree down!

Pauline holds Mrs Lucas's hand.

Mrs Lucas I've fallen for somebody myself. I may as well tell you. Make you feel better perhaps.

Pauline Oh, I'm so glad. What's his name?

Mrs Lucas *Her* name is Glenys.

Pauline drops Mrs Lucas's hand.

Pauline Oh, I see.

Mrs Lucas You're shocked, aren't you?

Pauline Well, I am a bit. You don't expect it in a cul-de-sac somehow.

Pauline grabs Mrs Lucas's hand again.

Mrs Lucas	You never know about people. There are things you don't know about him. Will you take Adrian with you?
Pauline	I don't know. It's hard to uproot a kid, they're not like trees.
Mrs Lucas	But at least I'll see these grow. Goodnight. Good luck with Derek.

She pushes the wheelbarrow off stage. It has got dark.

Pauline	Good luck with Glenys.

George enters the garden, shining a torch.

George	Pauline!
Pauline	I'm here!
George	What are you doing standing in the dark?
Pauline	I've been talking to Mrs Lucas. About trees.
George	You're shivering. Come in, love. I've turned the thermostat up. It's lovely and warm at home. And I've got Jim Reeves on the turntable.
Pauline	What's Adrian doing?
George	He's in his room. Why?
Pauline	Do you think he'd miss me, if I died, or went away?
George	Have you been drinking, Pauline? Of course he'd bloody miss you. You're his mother. (*Pause.*) You haven't got any health problems you've not told me about, have you?
Pauline	No.
George	What's all this silly slobber about dying and going away for then?
Pauline	I'm just being daft, take no notice.
George	You've not been yourself lately.

Pauline speaks quickly:

Pauline	George, I'm in love with another man.

A long pause.

George	You mean other than me?
Pauline	Yes. I said *another* man.
	A small pause.
George	What's his name?
Pauline	Derek.
George	Thank god for that. It's usually someone you know. You'll have to give me a minute, Pauline. My body's stopped working. I can't move it.
	George is motionless.
Pauline	Derek is Bimbo, Mr Lucas. We're standing in his back garden.
	George gives a long anguished moan of despair and anger.
	He drops to his knees.
Pauline	Don't, love, don't. Oh, I'm so sorry. I wish it hadn't happened.
	George clasps Pauline's legs.
George	Don't leave me, Pauline.
Pauline	I've got to. I can't live next door to the man I love!
	George is desperate.
George	I'll build you a car port, then you can go and see him without getting wet.
Pauline	We'll have to talk it over in a civilised manner, the three of us. We're all intelligent people, we can work something out. Tonight.
	She starts to go off.
George	Where are you going?
Pauline	To tell Bimbo.
George	What about Adrian?
	Pauline is crying.
Pauline	I can't tell him. You'll have to. I told him about his mouse!
	Pauline goes off.

George shouts after her.

George What bloody mouse? (*Pause.*) I'll kill him. I'll ram his policies and his third party fire and thefts down his throat. I'll fully comprehensively break his neck! She's married to me! I've got a paper to prove it!

He continues sadly:

But there's nothing in the small print to say she can't go off with anybody else.

George begins to sing a song in the style of Jim Reeves:

Your Hair of Gold

George Your hair of gold, your eyes of baby blue
How could I ever face a life without you?
Your lips so sweet, your touch so tender –
You know I surrender to everything that you do.

Your glance, your smile – they haunt me all the while:
Sleeping or waking you're always there beside me:
Your laugh, your kiss – my riches forever:
You know that I'll never let you go from my heart.

George goes off as the lights go up to show Adrian standing in the hall.

Adrian My mother has arranged what she called a civilised meeting. Mr Lucas is going to be there. Naturally I am not invited. I'm going to listen at the door.

Adrian listens at the living-room door. The lights go up in the living room to show Pauline, Mr Lucas and George arguing.

George paces about, he looks haggard. Pauline watches him anxiously. Mr Lucas starts talking. George hangs his head. Pauline gets up to comfort him. George pushes her away. He takes a handkerchief out of his pocket and wipes his eyes. Pauline talks, her eyes down.

The civilised meeting broke up when my father found out how long my mother and Mr Lucas had been in love. And when my mother disclosed that she was leaving for Sheffield with Mr Lucas, my father became uncivilised and started fighting! In the *front* garden. All the neighbours came out to watch.

Adrian runs up to the first floor.

George and Mr Lucas mime fighting. Pauline mimes trying to break it up. Mr Lucas escapes into the front garden. George and Pauline run after him. Adrian hangs out of the window, watching.

George shouts:

George   You're not having her! She's my wife!

He rugby tackles Mr Lucas and brings him down.

Pauline   Don't hurt him, George!

George   Hurt him – I'll kill him!

Mr Lucas gets up and hits George on the jaw.

Pauline   Don't hurt him, Bimbo!

Mr Lucas   She belongs to me now!

Pauline gets between the two but is unable to stop George head butting Mr Lucas.

Pauline   It was supposed to be a civilised meeting.

George and Mr Lucas stagger in opposite directions.

Mr Lucas   Ah! He's hurt me, Pauline! He's broken my nose. I shall look like Henry Cooper.

Pauline   Go on! Finish each other off! Kill him, George! Get stuck in! You're uncivilised, the pair of you!

Mr Lucas   Steady on Pauline.

George chases Mr Lucas off.

Pauline is distraught:

Pauline   I don't care any more. I'm going to Sheffield with him or without him.

She screams.

I can see you looking through your net curtains, Mrs O'Leary!

Pauline runs off.

Adrian is looking through the front bedroom window.

Adrian   All the people looked up and saw me so I looked especially sad. I expect the experience will give me a trauma at some stage in the future. I'm all right at the moment, but you never know.

Scene Eleven

The lights go up to show George in the bathroom bathing his face, and Pauline in the bedroom packing a suitcase. Adrian is in his bedroom with the dog. They sing the following:

Family Trio

Adrian   Two o'clock in the morning:
Leicester's asleep as sound as a log:
I count sheep in the stillness,
As we lie awake – just me and the dog.

Pauline   Maybe this is the right time to
Find out what I am good for,
And what would be really good for me –
Maybe ... maybe
I'm more, more than I bargained for,
Braver than I believed I could
Be – I'm free to become ...who knows?
We'll see, maybe ...

George   Your hair of gold, your eyes of baby blue –
How could I ever face a life without you?

Adrian   Five o'clock in the morning:
No one's about, not even a mouse:

All peace and quiet on the outside –
Who would believe there's a war in our house?

George and Pauline sing simultaneously:

Maybe this is the time to	Your hair of gold, your eyes of baby blue –
Find out what I am good for,	How could I ever face a life without you
And what would be really good for me	Your lips so sweet, your touch so tender –
Maybe ... maybe	You know I surrender to everything that you do.
I'm more, more than I bargained for,	
Braver than I believed I could	
Be – I'm free to become ... who cares?	
We'll see, maybe ...	

George and Pauline repeat their verses as Adrian sings the following:

Five o'clock in the morning:
No one's about, not even a mouse:
Nothing moves in the silence –
Who would believe there's a war in our house?

**Adrian/Pauline/
George** Maybe ... maybe ... maybe ... maybe ... we'll see.

Blackout.

Act Two

Scene One

*Adrian is in his bedroom writing in his diary.
George is downstairs in the living-room slumped
on the sofa. He is unshaven.*

Voice over.

Adrian Tuesday March 31st. My mother has gone to
Sheffield with Mr Lucas. She had to drive
because Mr Lucas couldn't see out of his black
eyes. I have informed the school secretary of
my mother's desertion, she was very kind and
gave me a form to give to my father; it is for free
school dinners. We are now a single parent
family. Nigel has asked Barry Kent to stop
menacing me for a few weeks. Barry Kent said
he would think about it.

*Adrian comes downstairs and sits down opposite
George.*

George I don't know what I did wrong. I never hit her. I
was tempted, but I never actually got round to
…

George punches the air viciously, landing a blow.

I put my money on the table every Friday night
without fail; not all, but most. I've got a temper
…

He loses his temper.

… all right, I admit it! It's a fault I've got and I
shout a bit, but I mean nothing by it.

He becomes calmer.

I thought she'd got used to it. Has she gone
because I'm losing my hair? (Pause.) I know I've
let myself go downhill – No I've not, she has.
She stopped sewing my buttons on and
stitching my turnups. And I can't remember the

last time she bought me any Cherry Blossom.
They've noticed at work; a memo was passed
about my shoes. When you tell the punters how
much the storage heater'll cost, they look at the
floor. You can lose a sale because of the lack of a
good shine. (*Pause*.) I know things weren't too
hot physically, but it was her fault! She put a
barrier between us. She read *The Guardian* in
bed at night. Even worse, she even sometimes
read bits out! 'Listen to what Jill Tweedie says
about men' – she'd say. It was never
complimentary. It's Jill Tweedie's fault that
Pauline's gone. Her and that Greasy Greer!
(*Pause*.) So why's she gone off with *another man*?

Grandma enters, taking her hat and coat off.

Grandma   Hello, Adrian, you look pale. You're not
constipated are you? I've got a bottle of syrup of
figs in my bag if you are.

Adrian   No, it's all right. I went this morning.

Grandma   Good boy. Where's Pauline, George?

George and Adrian exchange a glance.

George   She's in Sheffield.

Grandma   Who does she know in Sheffield?

George   Mr Lucas from next door.

Grandma   But Mr Lucas from next door lives next door,
doesn't he?

George   No, not any more he doesn't. He lives in
Sheffield – with Pauline.

Grandma   Do you mean that they're living. . .together?

George   Yes.

Grandma   In sin?

George   Yes.

Grandma   I knew it! I always said she was wanton. Thank
the good Lord your father never lived to see
this day. It would have killed him.

She sits. Adrian goes off to fetch the tea things.

George	It's hit me hard, Mum.
Grandma	How could she bear to tear herself away from that wonderful boy? It just proves how inhuman she is.
George	I keep seeing them together, in Sheffield … making love in front of a knife and fork factory.
Grandma	You're well rid of her, George. She never cleaned behind the cooker.
George	I should have taken her out more. She loved Chinese food. The odd prawn ball wouldn't have hurt me.

Adrian enters carrying a tea tray with milk carton, sugar bag, mugs and a packet of biscuits.

Grandma speaks to Adrian:

Grandma	What's that supposed to be?
Adrian	It's the tea tray, Grandma.
Grandma	I'll excuse you this once, Adrian, it must have been unsettling when your mother left home. But it's no good descending to the level of animals. Now, go back into the kitchen and do it properly; milk jug, sugar bowl, doily for the biscuits, cups and saucers and apostle spoons.

Adrian goes out to the kitchen with the tray.

Grandma	How's *he* taken it?
George	I don't know, he's not said. I can still smell her perfume on the sheets!

George starts to sniffle.

Grandma	Right. I'll have *them* in the wash tomorrow. Now, go upstairs and have a shave. You may think it's amusing to look like a communist but I don't. I know you've had a bit of a shock …
George	A bit of a shock! My world has fallen apart! I'm a broken man!

George cries.

Grandma	You've no gumption, George. Your father

shaved every day of his life. Even when he was in the trenches at Ypres. Sometimes he had to stop the rats from eating his shaving soap. He was even shaved in his coffin by the undertaker, so if the dead can shave, then there's no excuse for the living.

George   I don't want to go on living, not without Pauline. I love her, Mum.

Grandma   Do you want me to smack your bum? You might be 41 but you're not too old. I won't have you giving way to your emotions like this – it's not healthy. All this silly slobber about *love*. It's decency that counts. Keeping a clean front and paying your bills on time. Where's love got you, eh? I shall leave the room until you've pulled yourself together.

Grandma goes off to the kitchen. Lights on kitchen.

Adrian is pouring sugar into a bowl.

Grandma   I'm sorry to see your father in such a state.

Adrian   He found one of my mother's earrings down the back seat of the car this morning. He kept staring at it with a funny look in his eyes ... Then he asked me if I missed my mother. I said 'Of course I do, but life must go on!'

Grandma   Quite right.

Adrian   But he said: 'I don't see why.' I took this to mean that he was suicidal. So I took his razor and all the sleeping pills from out of the bathroom. Just to be on the safe side.

Grandma   Good boy.

They enter the living-room.

Grandma   It's times like this I realise what a privilege it was to be married to your grandad. There was no suicide threats or adultery in *our* marriage. We just plodded on day after day for 40 years. I wouldn't say we were especially happy, but then again we weren't unhappy either. Your grandad

was a quiet man; he hated noise and
disagreements, so there were no rows. But I
knew when he was upset; he used to rap his
fingers on the mangle outside the back door.

She demonstrates on the coffee table.

Adrian   Yes, he used to do that a lot when I came round.

Grandma   Yes, well you used to get on his nerves a bit –
always asking questions.

Adrian   He never answered any.

Grandma   How could he? He didn't know anything. I used
to read bits out of the newspaper to him
sometimes, but he'd say: 'Don't bother me with
the outside world, May.' It upset him, you see. I
suppose you could say he was a timid man.

Grandma breaks into the following song:

Your Dead Grandad

Grandma   I don't recall
Just when he popped the question:
He bought a ring – I've still got that:
We hired a hall, he hired a top hat –
He looked a toff, your dead Grandad.

Adrian   Can I have a biscuit please Grandma?

Grandma continues singing:

Grandma   He never had to tell me that he loved me –
We had no use for sentimental chat:
I'd wash the dishes – he would dry,
We dug the garden – time passed by:
I miss him still, your dead Grandad.

Adrian   Grandma, can I … ?

*Adrian reaches for a biscuit. Grandma slaps his
hand.*

She sings:

Grandma   We never made excuses for bad manners,
No psycho-this or socio-that at all:

Folks were either sane or mad,
We'd no posh words for being bad –
But he was good, your dead Grandad.

George!

George Yes, Mum.

Grandma Would you mind driving me up to the garden centre in the car? Only I'm running low on poisons.

George gets the coats.

George No – I don't mind.

Grandma Good, and it'll take you out of yourself, won't it? Do you want to come, Adrian?

Adrian I'd love to but Nigel's coming round to collect a book.

Grandma kisses Adrian.

Grandma Well, bye bye love. And don't fret about your mother. You know what they say: 'The bad penny gathers no moss.'

Nigel enters as Grandma and George go off.

George Go through, he's in there.

Adrian Oh you're here.

Nigel Yeah, you got it?

Adrian Yes.

He takes a magazine called Big and Bouncy *from under a cushion and gives it to Nigel, who flicks through it and puts it under his jumper.*

Nigel God, your furniture! It's like reject corner at MFI in here. I get a shock every time I come in.

Adrian is apologetic:

Adrian I know. It was brilliant staying at your house last weekend, Nigel. It's really opened my eyes. Without knowing it I've been living in poverty for the last fourteen years. Perhaps if *my* father had built a formica cocktail cabinet in *our* lounge, my mother would still be here.

Nigel　I doubt it. Your mum left because your dad went round looking like a scruffbag. You can't expect a woman to put up with it. In fact, Adrian, if you don't do something about your own personal image, you're going to end up sentenced to a life of chastity.

Nigel begins to sing:

Get It Right!

Nigel　Adrian Mole, why d'you look such a right arsehole?
I've never seen anyone dress worse!
Your bottoms are flared and your boots curl up like they're scared
And your duffel coat positively festers!
Your jumper is straight off the tip –
Do you wear it in bed when you kip?
Oh Moley, you're wholly, completely – words defeat me!
Try Lacoste, Doc Martens, some Farahs you'd look smart in –
If you want to wear clothes – get them right!

Your bike's a disgrace – you need a BMX or a racer
With a speedo and ten gears like my one:
This Walkman will surprise you, got a built-in graphic equaliser
With these new lightweight 'phones – why not try one?
This digital Seiko's for you
If you want to play chess in the loo:
Oh, Mole-face, it's as simple as squeezing a pimple!
Ask for Raleigh, or Sony, Ticini, Cerutti –
Whatever you get – get it right!

Your taste, I must say, falls far short of a true gourmet –

You live on baked beans and fish fingers:
In a hurry a curry from a tin saves a lot of
worry,
But it does have a strong pong that lingers:
The best things are subtle, not loud,
And known to a few, not the crowd:
Not your Tizer from Tesco – Frascati, *al fresco*!
Say Martini, say Campari, say Adidas, say Atari,
Say Honda, Sekonda, aerobics, Jane Fonda –
If you want to get on – get it right!

Anyway, must rush, I'm seeing Pandora at four
o'clock.We're having wholemeal crumpets in
front of the log fire.

Adrian   You're dead lucky Nigel. What's she like to go
out with?

Nigel   To tell you the truth she's not much cop. I'm
used to birds that give it out, talking of which
have you heard from your mum?

Adrian   I had a postcard telling me that she'd found a
flat – she lives at 69a President Carter Walk,
Sheffield. Why can't she write a letter like any
normal person? Why should the postman be
able to read my confidential business? I've
asked my father if I can go.

Nigel   What's he say?

Adrian imitates George:

Adrian   Yeah, providing she sends the train fare.

Adrian moves off stage.

Scene Two

Voice over.

Adrian   It was the first time I'd been on a train on my
own. I'm certainly spreading my wings lately.
(*Pause.*) Sheffield looks just like Leicester really.
I didn't see any knife and fork factories. So I
suppose Margaret Thatcher has closed them all
down.

Pauline and Mr Lucas's Sheffield flat.

Adrian and Pauline come in with shopping. They are met by Mr Lucas.

Mr Lucas Had a good day?

He goes to Pauline and kisses her then puts his arms around her from the back. He almost touches her breasts but Pauline holds his hands firmly.

Pauline *I* did.

She turns to Adrian.

Did you, love?

Adrian Yes, thank you.

Pauline There's no need to be so polite! I'm your mother – remember?

Mr Lucas What did you get up to then, young Adrian?

Adrian turns away from Mr Lucas.

Adrian We had a Chinese Businessman's lunch, then we went to Habitat to buy a lampshade for ...

He looks at Pauline.

Pauline Our bedroom. Then we saw a Monty Python film – it was all about the life of Jesus.

Adrian speaks to Pauline:

Adrian I felt guilty laughing!

Pauline And I got him some nice new trousers – tight ones!

Mr Lucas kisses Pauline's hair, neck and lips.

Pauline Don't!

She pushes Mr Lucas away.

Adrian I'm going to try my new trousers on.

Pauline All right, love.

Adrian goes off.

Mr Lucas Did you notice? He didn't look me in the eye once.

Pauline He's bound to feel a bit strange. I do myself.

Mr Lucas grabs Pauline.

Pauline Oh let go of me! I'm fed up with you mauling me about. I feel like the last chicken in Sainsbury's! How would you feel if a man was messing about with your mother?

Mr Lucas I'd be very surprised. She's been dead for five years.

Pauline There's so much I don't know about you. The false teeth came as a surprise.

Mr Lucas I've only got the four.

Pauline Yes, but at the front. Don't take them out again, will you? Not at bed time.

Mr Lucas I'm glad you brought up the subject of bed time. When do you think we'll be able to – er – get together?

Pauline (*pause*): I can't. I just can't. Not with that child here.

Mr Lucas But it's our honeymoon, Paulie.

Pauline Would you mind not calling me 'Paulie'? It reminds me of childhood illnesses. My name's *Pauline*, Derek.

Mr Lucas Oh, I see. So it's Derek now is it, Mrs Mole?

Pauline Yes and I don't think it will ever be Mrs Pauline Lucas either.

Mr Lucas But you promised to marry me! You said you'd get a divorce. You've been using me. Oh God, I feel dirty!

Pauline Oh try and pull yourself together, Derek. You sound like something out of Barbara Cartland!

Adrian enters. He is wearing tight black trousers. The labels are hanging off.

Mr Lucas Who's a super trendy, then?

Pauline Oh you do look nice, Adrian. They really suit you. Turn round, Doesn't he look grown up!

Adrian turns.

Mr Lucas Oh yes, the birds will be after you now, eh Adrian?

Adrian blushes, looks uncomfortable.

Adrian   Can you take the labels off please, Mum?

Mr Lucas takes a Swiss army knife out of his apron pocket.

Mr Lucas   Allow me. Don't know how I survived without my Swiss army knife. Now, where's the scissors?

He fumbles with the blades.

Mr Lucas   Course they're wasted on the Swiss – never fought a decent war.

He is still fumbling.

Very good for emergencies.

Adrian and Pauline watch as he fumbles.

Pauline   Slow emergencies.

Mr Lucas   Give me a chance, Pauline!

He is still fumbling.

Mr Lucas   You can saw through a tree with a Swiss army knife, Adrian. In fact, we'll have a drive out to the countryside tomorrow and I'll prove it to you.

Adrian replies coldly:

Adrian   It's against the law to saw trees down.

Mr Lucas   Bloody bureaucrats!

Pauline   Yes, it'll do us all good to get out of here and get some fresh air in our lungs.

She rips the labels from Adrian's trousers with her bare hands.

Mr Lucas hands the Swiss army knife to Adrian.

Mr Lucas   I want you to have this, Adrian. As a sort of memento of your visit which sincerely I hope will be the first of many. We both want you to regard this as your second home.

Pauline   Oh Bimbo, what a lovely thing to do.

Adrian   Sorry, but I can't accept it. I've turned pacifist.

Mr Lucas sounds martyred:

Mr Lucas   I don't mind admitting I'm very, very hurt. I

	would have given an arm and a leg for one of these when I was a lad.

He goes off.

Pauline   Adrian – why didn't you accept it graciously? He's trying ever so hard to be nice to you.

Adrian   Mum, there's things you ought to know about Creep Lucas.

Pauline   What?

Adrian   There's a new family moved into his house and the bloke, Mr Singh, he found this stack of horrible magazines under the lino in the bathroom.

Pauline   So?

Adrian   Well, they belonged to Mr Lucas. He's a pervert! You'll have to come home.

Pauline   What were these magazines called?

Adrian   *Amateur Photographer.*

Pauline   So, Bimbo's interested in photography – it doesn't mean he's Jack the Ripper!

Adrian   Mum you'll have to come home soon. Dad's falling in love with another woman.

Pauline   What's her name?

Adrian   Doreen Slater.

Pauline laughs.

Pauline   Oh – Dopey Doreen! Is she still making the rounds? My god, she's got some staying power!

Pauline goes off. Adrian goes to his house. He goes upstairs and looks at George's bed.

Voice over.

Adrian   My father said he had had Doreen Slater to tea. By the state of the house I should think he'd had her for breakfast, dinner and tea! I have never seen the woman, but from the evidence she left behind, I know she has got bright red hair, wears orange lipstick and sleeps on the left side of the bed. What a homecoming!

Scene Three

Bert Baxter's house. Bert is in his chair. Toothless.
Bert is looking for his teeth.

Bert Where are yer? Where are yer?

He shouts offstage to Adrian:

Bert I know I 'ad 'em this mornin' but then I took 'em
out to give me gums a rest. I've looked in the
lavvy but they're not on the window sill where I
usually leaves 'em.

Adrian enters.

Adrian I wish you hadn't rung me at school, Bert. I got
into trouble. Scruton went mad.

Bert Scruton? That the headmaster? Stuck-up git! I
told him a few things. You haven't found 'em,
then?

Adrian No, I've looked everywhere.

Bert I shall have to find 'em. They've got sentimental
value: belonged to me father. I've had them
teeth since 1946 and besides I shall starve. I
can't chew me beetroot. 'Ave another look,
there's a good lad. And see how Sabre is will
you? He's been quiet all morning. It ain't like 'im.

Adrian He's chewing something in his kennel. He's all
right.

Adrian goes off.

*Bert is struggling to get out of his chair but can't
do it.*

Bert speaks to his legs:

Bert Come on me old beauties. Don't let me down!

He sits back.

*Adrian enters with Bert's teeth held between
thumb and finger.*

Bert You've found 'em! Good lad. Where was they?

Adrian In Sabre's kennel.

Bert laughs.

Bert He's a bugger! Give 'em a swill under the tap.

Adrian is horrified.

Adrian Bert, no!

Bert I can't put 'em straight back into me mouth after a dog's been chewing 'em all night, can I? What's up with you, ain't you heard of hygiene?

Adrian goes out to Bert's kitchen.

Talking of which, ain't it time you came round and did a bit o'cleaning? Tomorrow will be all right.

Adrian comes back, drying the teeth on a tea towel.

Adrian I can't come tomorrow, my mother's coming home to talk about who gets custody.

Bert Who gets custard?

Adrian Custody, Bert.

He gives Bert the teeth. Bert puts them into his mouth.

Adrian addresses the audience:

Adrian This is the most revolting thing I have ever seen, and I'm no stranger to squalor.

Bert Be a good lad an' make me a beetroot sandwich up will you?

Adrian OK.

Adrian makes a sandwich.

Bert So, your mum and dad are gettin' a divorce are they?

Adrian replies sadly:

Adrian Yes.

Bert I don't hold with divorce. I was married for 35 miserable years, so why should anybody else get away with it? (*Pause.*) Did I ever show you a photo of my wife?

Adrian No, Bert.

Bert Pass us the photo album then. It's in the pouffe.

Adrian passes the album.

Bert opens the album.

Bert That's her. (*Pause.*) Course it were in the days before they had plastic surgery. (*Pause.*)

Adrian She looks a bit like. . .

Bert An 'oss? Yes, I know, funny that. I never realised until I stopped working with 'osses and went to work on the railways.

Adrian I'd better go now, Bert.

Bert No, stay a bit longer, lad. Here – you seen this Bible? Saved my life this did. I had it in me breast pocket when a Jerry sniper shot at me. See that? It's a bullet hole. Saved my life. It was a miracle!

Adrian But this Bible was printed in 1958, Bert.

Bert Well, I said it was a miracle!

Bert goes out. Adrian crosses to the Mole living-room.

Scene Four

George Mole is hoovering the living-room. He is singing 'Your Hair of Gold'. He is looking cheerful. He's tidied himself up.

George Adrian, I'm just off to fetch your mother's flowers. Won't be long. Carry on cleaning up.

Adrian makes sure that his father has gone then he takes a tape measure and looks round furtively. He takes a tiny notebook out and measures his thing and records the measurement. An Electricity Board official starts banging on the front door. Adrian drops the tape measure. He quickly adjusts his dress. He lets the official in.

Offical Electricity Board. You owe us £97.79.

Adrian That's a lot.

Official Yes, it is isn't it? And it's obviously more than you can pay. So, I've come to cut you off.

He enters the hall.

Adrian   But you can't do that! We need electricity for life's essentials, like the television and stereo!

The official opens his tool box.

Official   It's people like you what are sapping the country's strength. Where's the meter cupboard?

Adrian   There.

The official goes to the cupboard and fiddles around. The Mole lights go down.

The official adopts a mournful expression.

Official   Do you think I enjoy doing this son?

The official puts his hand on Adrian's shoulder.

Adrian   No, I'm sure you don't.

Official   Well you'd be wrong because I do! Good morning.

George enters. His arms full of flowers. He passes the official.

George   Morning. Would you like a cup of tea?

Official   No thank you, sir. I never fraternise with the enemy.

He leaves.

George laughs.

George   It's nice to know that officials have got a sense of humour.

He speaks to Adrian:

Stick these in a milk bottle, I'll finish the hoovering – she'll be here soon.

He switches the Hoover on. No power.

What the bloody hell's up with this?

He kicks the Hoover.

Have you been playing at Daleks again?

Adrian   No. Dad. . .we've been cut off. You haven't paid the bill. You should have put it away every week, in a jug, like Grandma does.

George   She'll be here soon and I've still got bits on my

shag pile! You should have refused entry, you
stupid. . .

He swears under his breath.

Pauline enters.

Pauline   George! Adrian!

George   Pauline! Love, you look wonderful!

Mr Lucas enters.

What's he doing here? I thought Adrian's custody
was being decided between the two of us?

Mr Lucas   Where Pauline goes, I go.

Pauline   It's gloomy in here, George. Can't we have a light
on?

Adrian   No. We've had our electricity cut off.

George   Temporarily.

Pauline responds kindly:

Pauline   Well, I'm not surprised you can't pay the bills,
George – these flowers must have cost a fortune.

Mr Lucas   If you want to borrow a ton, George ...

George   All I want from you, Lucas, is my wife.

Pauline   But apart from having no electricity, you're
keeping the house beautifully, George.

Mr Lucas offers Adrian a fiver.

Mr Lucas   Here, Adrian, go and buy some candles. This
meeting might go on all night. We can't negotiate
in the dark.

Adrian   Shall I, Dad?

George   We've got no choice, son. I'm skint.

*Adrian goes to his room. The lights go down on the
living-room and up on Adrian's bedroom.*

Voice over:

The arguing went on for ages. In fact until it was
time to light the candles. Mr Lucas spilt candle
wax on his new shoes. It was the only cheerful
incident in a tragic day.

Pauline walks off followed by Mr Lucas.

George Mole is talking on the phone to Doreen Slater.

George   Doreen, I know I said it was all over. But I can't stop thinking about you. . .Baby. Thanks, warm the bed up.

George puts the phone down, grabs the flowers and goes out quickly.

Adrian sits on the bed singing the following song to his dog:

Dog
('The House Where I Live' reprise)

Adrian   You are my only true friend,
Always here at the end
Of a traumatic day:
I'm used to your slobb'ring embrace
And your lop-sided face. . .is OK

Oh Dog, never gave you a name,
Still I'm glad that you came
To the house where I live.

You are so easy to please
And occasional fleas
Don't detract from your charms:
I s'pose you're a bit of a mess,
But I couldn't care less – in my arms,

Oh Dog, you're so floppy and warm!
We'll both weather the storm
In the house where we live.

Scene Five

The candlelit living-room. George and Adrian are sitting around a small primus stove. They are wearing scarves and gloves. George is reading Playboy. Adrian is reading a hardback book, using a torch.

George	What's that you're reading?
Adrian	*Hard Times* by Charles Dickens.
George	D'you want some more beans, son?
	He hands him a Heinz tin and spoon.
Adrian	No thanks, I don't like them cold.
George	Y'know this is good training for when civilisation collapses. You'll thank me one day.
Adrian	Oh, I don't mind. In fact, it's quite nice. (*Pause.*) Dad, what do you think my chances are of becoming a vet?
George	Nil. (*a*) You're no good at science. (*b*) You don't want to be a vet, son, they spend half their lives with their hands stuck up cows' bums.
	A noise off.
	Grandma enters the house, she gropes about in the dark.
Grandma	George, are you there?
George	Blow the candles out! It's your grandma!
Adrian	She's bound to find us, Dad. We may as well surrender.
	Adrian goes to Grandma's aid.
	Grandma tries to switch on the lights.
Grandma	George! I know you're there, I can hear voices.
Adrian	In here, Grandma!
	Grandma gropes into the room.
Grandma	Whose idea was it to sit in the dark?
Adrian	The Electricity Board's.
Grandma	So, you've stopped paying your bills now, have you?
George	Pauline managed the money. I don't know how to do it, Mum.
Grandma	It's quite simple. All you do is put it away in jugs. Gas in a pink jug. Electricity in a blue and so on. How much do you owe?

Adrian   £97.79 pence.

Grandma   My god! £97.00. You must have a leak
              somewhere! I'll call the Board out first thing
              tomorrow.

              *Grandma takes a cheque book out of her bag and
              writes a cheque by candlelight.*

              Adrian speaks to George in a loud whisper.

Adrian   You shouldn't be taking money from a
              pensioner.

              George hits Adrian round the head.

Grandma   Now I shan't be able to restock my freezer. You
              know I like to buy half a cow a year.

              Grandma gives George a cheque.

George   I'm sorry, Mum. Thank you. I'll pay you back.

              Grandma speaks to Adrian:

Grandma   Now what's this I hear about Barry Kent beating
              you up for money?

Adrian   Who told you?

Grandma   It's all round the Evergreen Club.

George   I've been to see his father. But he wouldn't
              listen. I daren't push it any further, he's like an
              ape, Mum. He's got more hair on his knuckles
              than I've got on my head.

Grandma   Where does this Barry Kent boy live?

Adrian   Number Thirteen Corporation Row. You're not
              thinking of going are you?

              Adrian stands.

George   Leave it to the police, Mum.

              George stands.

              Grandma is contemptuous:

Grandma   The police! We Moles fight our own battles!

              She straightens her back and leaves.

              George goes off.

              Adrian speaks to the audience:

Adrian She was gone one hour and seven minutes. She came in, took her coat off. Fluffed her hair out. Took £27.18 from the anti-mugger belt around her waist. She said 'He won't bother you again, Adrian, but if he does, let me know'. Then she got the tea ready, pilchards, tomatoes and ginger cake. I bought her a box of diabetic chocolates from the chemists as a token of my esteem.

Scene Six

Lights go up in the kitchen where Doreen Slater is making tea.

Voice over.

Adrian My father rang Doreen Slater up and asked her to come round. It was quite a shock to see her for the first time. Why my father wants to have carnal knowledge of her I can't imagine. She is as thin as a stick insect. She has got no bust and no bum. She is just straight all the way up and all the way down.

The phone rings. Doreen picks up the phone in the hall.

Pauline in a housecoat on the other side of the stage is holding a phone.

Doreen Hello, George Mole's residence.

Pauline To whom am I speaking at 7.30 in the morning?

Doreen I'm Miss Doreen Slater. To whom am *I* speaking?

Pauline Mrs Pauline Mole. Could I speak to my son please?

Doreen I don't know if he's up. I've only just got out of bed myself.

Pauline Out of my husband's bed, I presume?

Adrian comes downstairs.

Doreen I don't see what it's got to do with you. You're the one that left. You've upset me now.

She speaks to Adrian:

Doreen   Your mother's on the phone.

Adrian grabs the phone.

Adrian   Mum?

Pauline   What's Doreen Slater doing in *my* house?

Adrian   Dad sent for her. Something terrible's happened.

Pauline   It's not the dog?

Adrian   No, it's Dad. He's been made redundant from his job. He'll be on the dole! Mum – how will we manage on the pittance the Government gives us? The dog will have to go. It costs 35 pence a day, not counting Winalot! Mum – I'm now a single parent child with a father on the dole. Social Security will be buying my shoes!

Pauline   Calm down, Adrian. I'll buy your shoes. Oh my god, what next? How's he taken it?

Adrian   He's having a nervous breakdown I think. He watches *Playschool*!

Pauline   That's nothing to worry about. He's always watched *Playschool* when he got the chance.

She speaks fondly:

He used to love guessing the shape of the windows. Oh, I wish I were there right now.

Adrian   So do I, Mum. Come home.

Pauline   I can't Adrian. I haven't found what I'm looking for yet. 'Bye pet.

The lights go down on Pauline. She goes off.

Doreen   Well, what's happening? Is she coming home or what? Only I need to know. I'm having a new fireplace put in at my home.

Adrian   She's not coming back.

He puts the phone down.

Doreen   So does that mean I'm staying, then?

Adrian   I don't know. You'd better ask my dad.

Doreen   Only if I knew, I could cancel the fireplace.

Adrian   Hasn't *he* said anything?

Doreen   No, he doesn't talk. He doesn't do anything
and I mean anything. He's been rendered
impotent.

Adrian blanches.

He was all right before he was made redundant.
He was ever so good at it – you don't mind me
talking like this, do you? No, of course you
don't. In my day, adults didn't talk about … you
know …

She mouths 'sex'.

but now, it's all open and above board, isn't it?
You and your mates talk about it all the time,
don't you?

Adrian shakes his head.

Doreen   Have you noticed how much he's drinking and
smoking?

Adrian nods.

Adrian   Yes, I think he's going mental.

Doreen   I'm ever so worried about him, he's not sleeping
either, he just lies in bed with his arms folded
behind his head, staring at the ceiling. People
are talking about me, you know. Saying I've got
no morals. It's because my Maxwell was born
out of wedlock. but it's not my fault, is it? I'd
give anything to be in wedlock. It's just my bad
luck that I fall in love with married men. (*Pause.*)
Over and over again.

Adrian looks on with growing distaste.

Doreen begins to sing:

The Other Woman

Doreen   The other woman – *his* other woman:
I'm another woman in the hours he spends with
me:

'The other woman' – why does it bother me?
You'd think by now I'd play my old familiar role
with some good grace.

Now, for a week or two,
I'll pretend he'll stay with me –
Such hurried ecstasy!
Then she'll reappear, he'll say 'Sorry, my dear, it
was fun' –
And out will go the sun.

The other woman: who *is* 'the other woman'?
Who has shown concern for him? Deserves his
trust and love?
The other woman, *this* other woman,
While she ran out on him, without a thought,
without a backward glance:

Who came to rescue him,
Soothed away all his pain,
Made him feel brave again?
This other woman, who secretly knew from the
start
That he would break my heart.

Doreen goes upstairs.

Adrian speaks to the audience:

Adrian Doreen talks to me as if I was another adult
instead of her lover's son, aged fourteen, two
months and one day. I'm just about sick of so-
called adults. You would think that they would
be old enough to manage their lives a bit better,
but oh, no! They go about baring their sickly
emotions to anybody who will listen. All this
family trouble is sending me rebellious. In fact, I
wore red socks to school. It's strictly forbidden
but I don't care any more.

*Adrian shows his red socks to the audience then
walks to the school wall. Adrian stands between
Pandora, Nigel and another schoolgirl showing
off his red socks. Nigel's trousers are tucked into
his socks. Pandora's socks are lurex.*

Pandora	You're a true revolutionary, Adrian. When they come to write the history of school politics – your name will be in the index under 'M'.
Nigel	I was gob-smacked when I heard it was you who lead the revolt – I didn't think you were the revolting type!
Adrian	Well, I'm not really – in fact I can't help wishing that I'd worn my black socks the other day.
Pandora	Come on now, Adrian – no revisionism. Stand by your principles! Why should we be forced to wear the black socks of oppression?
Nigel	Come on then! Let's march on Scruton's office!
Adrian	But what if the GCE examiners find out about it next year? It could jeopardise our 'O' levels!
Nigel	He's got a point – a valid one.
Pandora	So am I going to face that fascist pig Scruton on my own?
Adrian	No, I'll come with you. I've started – so I'll finish. Are you coming, Nigel?
Nigel	It's a moral decision, isn't it?
Schoolgirl	Yes it is, darling.
Nigel	It's a bit hard to know what to do.
Pandora	If one's immoral – it's hard. But, if one has principles – then one has no choice.
	She starts to sing 'We Shall Not Be Moved'. The schoolgirl and the boys join in weakly but then with gathering strength. They march towards Scruton's office. Enter Scruton.
Scruton	Good morning.
Kids	Good morning, sir!
Scruton	Yes. I saw you making your way down the school drive. Very colourful, very foolhardy. What a brave little band you are! Now I should like you to hear the letter which I shall be sending to your parents.

'Dear Mr and Mrs. . .,

'It is my sad duty to inform you that your son – stroke – daughter has deliberately flaunted one of the rules of this school. I take an extremely serious view of this contravention. I am, therefore, suspending your son – stroke – daughter for a period of one week.

Pandora But, sir! What about our 'O' Levels. . .?

Scruton roars:

Scruton Quiet!

Everyone jumps.

Nigel Can we wear our black socks with a red stripe. Sir?

Scruton *No!* Your socks must be entirely, absolutely, incontrovertibly dense, midnight, black!

Scruton exits.

Pandora starts to cry.

Adrian Now look what he's done. Don't cry, Pandora. Aren't you going to try to stop her, Nigel?

Nigel No. She broke it off. She says I'm a philistine.

Nigel and the schoolgirl go off hand in hand.

Adrian pats Pandora's shoulder.

Adrian Don't cry. I've had a rejection letter from the BBC. Do you want to see it?

Pandora nods, she puts her head on Adrian's shoulder. He shows her the letter.

Music: 'Oh Pandora'.

Pandora and Adrian walk together.

Voice over.

Adrian Pandora and I are in love! It is official! She told Claire Neilson who told Nigel who told me. I told Claire to tell Pandora that I return her love. I can overlook the fact that Pandora smokes five Benson and Hedges a day and has her own lighter. When you are in love, such things cease to matter!

Adrian and Pandora are sitting on a school bench in the playground. They are not touching, but gazing into each other's eyes. They hold hands.

Pandora So, you didn't fall in love with me because of how I look – like everybody else?

Adrian Good god, no! That's dead sexist. No, it was because of your personal integrity. . .and your brain.

Pandora But, you don't think I'm ugly do you?

Adrian Ugly? You? You're brillo pad! You're the most desirable, erotic girl I've ever clapped eyes on!

Pandora Do you want to kiss me?

Adrian Well, of course I'd like to. . .I'm a bit out of practice though. . .

Pandora Do you do French?

Adrian Yes, I'm doing it for CSE.

Pandora French kissing!

Adrian Oh no. I usually just stick to the English!

Pandora and Adrian fumble a kiss. Pandora breaks away.

Pandora I don't think we're doing it properly. You need to open your lips just a little wider, Adrian.

Adrian Sorry.

Pandora Let's try again.

They kiss. Pandora breaks away.

Pandora Well, we've got plenty of time to practise. (*Pause.*) So when did you fall in love with me?

Adrian When I saw you playing netball.

Pandora I fell in love with your red socks first!

Adrian is disappointed.

Adrian Oh. . .

Pandora Your socks were enormously significant. You see, I'm a radical and I'm going to devote my whole life to changing our spiritually bankrupt society.

Adrian I'll help you if you like.

Pandora We can do it together!

Adrian And when we're married ...

Pandora moves away.

Pandora Married! But we're only fourteen, darling.

Adrian laughs.

Adrian I know we can't get married now, thanks to the stupid adults that make the laws, but, in two years time. . .

Pandora We'll be sixteen.

Adrian So we can get married. I know my dad would give me permission – he can't wait for me to leave home and my mother's left home anyway, so she can't prevent us. Don't worry, I wouldn't stop you working ... You could get a little job ... something part-time ... in a cakeshop, for instance.

Pandora stands.

Pandora is stern:

Pandora I am going to Oxford University. While there, I may occasionally enter a cake shop, but I will be buying a granary loaf. I will certainly not be *selling* one!

Adrian So you don't want to marry me and have twins?

Pandora I don't want to marry anybody!

Adrian Not ever?

Pandora No! I shall live in sin.

Adrian With me?

Pandora With several people I expect ... in the course of a lifetime ... Music 'Oh Pandora'.

During the song, Adrian behaves like a Latin lover.

Oh, Pandora

Adrian Oh, Pandora, I adore ... ya;
From the first day that I saw ya
I felt destiny called,
I knew I was enthralled
By your aura of love – my Pandora!

Always wondered how it would be:
This is passion as it should be!
Your lips smoulder with fire,
Your eyes melt with desire!
Take me higher and higher, my Pandora!

We'll get married straight away,
Find a cottage by a stream
With a private wishing-well
Where I can dream
Of my Pandora ...

Pandora Haven't done my physics homework:
There's that film I want to see on El Salvador –
It must be Channel Four:
There's so much I have to do
If I am to fulfil my potential –
Mustn't waste a second of my time!

Get my 'O's and 'A's – the Oxford!
Take a double first in Law and Economy –
Dead right for an MP!
Spare an afternoon a week
For a lover or two, but no attachment,
Nothing to deflect me from my course!

Pandora and Adrian sing simultaneously:

Two hearts beat in
  unison,
Two souls joined in
  perfect peace:
Our two bodies cry
  out loud
For release ...
Oh, please Pandora   Haven't done my physics
  – I implore ya   homework:

From the first day
   that I saw ya
I felt destiny called,
I knew I was
   enthralled
By your aura of
   love – my
Pandora!

My Pandora,
My Pandora,
Oh, my Pandora!

There's that film I want to
   see on El Salvador –
It must be Channel Four:
There's so much I have to do
If I am to fulfil my potential –
Mustn't waste a second of
   my time!
Must go …
Must go…
Mustn't waste a second of
   my time!

Pandora leaves Adrian on his knees.

Voice over.

Adrian My precious love leaves these shores tomorrow. I am going to the airport to see her off. I hope her plane won't suffer from metal fatigue. I have just checked the world map to see where Tunisia is and I am most relieved to see that Pandora won't have to fly through the Bermuda Triangle.

Adrian gets up and wanders about looking lost.

He speaks to the audience:

Adrian Wednesday July 22nd! Why haven't I had a postcard yet? What can have happened? Pandora! Pandora! Pandora!

He opens his notebook and clears his throat.

Oh! My love,
My heart is yearning
My mouth is dry,
My soul is burning.
You're in Tunisia
I am here.
Remember me and shed a tear.
Come back tanned and brown and healthy
You're lucky that your dad is wealthy.

She will be back in six days,

Adrian writes in his diary.

Voice over.

Adrian   Friday August 7th.
Moon's first quarter
I rang Tunisia whilst my father was in the bath.
He shouted down to ask whom I was phoning. I
told a lie. I said I was phoning the speaking clock.
Pandora's flight left safely. She should be home
around midnight.

*'Oh Pandora' music triumphant. Enter Pandora.
The lighting becomes romantic. There is an
emotional reunion with Adrian.*

Pandora   Adrian!

Adrian   Pandora!

They embrace.

Adrian   Did you have a good time?

Pandora   No. It was dreadful. Mummy was bitten by a
camel. Then the Tunisian baggage handlers
went on strike, but I told you that on the phone.
It *was* clever of you to ring me at Tunis airport.
Didn't your father mind?

Adrian   He doesn't know yet. I'm dreading the phone
bill coming.

Pandora   We're together again – that's all that matters.

They start to leave.

Adrian speaks to the audience:

Adrian   Went to Pandora's house. Had an emotional
reunion behind her father's tool shed.

They go off.

Scene Seven

Voice over.

Adrian   Monday October 5th.
Bert has been kidnapped by Social Services!
They are keeping him at the Alderman Cooper
Sunshine Home. I have been to see him. He

shares a room with an old man called Thomas
Bell. They have both got their names on their
ashtrays. Sabre has got a place in the RSPCA
hostel.

Bert is sitting in a wheelchair looking miserable.

*Matron enters with Queenie in a wheelchair: An
old lady with red hair and over-the-top make-up.*

Matron Mr Baxter, may I introduce a new guest to
'Smoker's Corner'?

Bert Guest? It ain't an hotel you're runnin', Matron!
It's an institution. What's run by the State. If I
was a *guest* I could have my dog wi' me.

Matron speaks to Queenie:

Matron Mr Baxter can be rather difficult, but we're
hoping he will settle down. (*Pause.*) Most of our
guests do. (*Pause.*) In time.

Queenie Well, I think he's right. We're not guests, are we?
None of us are here by choice.

She speaks to Bert:

Queenie What's your name, love?

Bert Bertram. What's yours?

Queenie Queenie.

Bert and Queenie look away from each other.

Matron Well, you're getting on like a house on fire,
aren't you? So, if you'll excuse me …

*Queenie and Bert stare hostilely at Matron as she
goes off.*

Bert What you doin' in ere? You ain't incapable of
lookin' after yourself, are you?

Queenie Not in my opinion, I'm not. But I'm told that I'm
going a bit doo-lally in the head.

Bert Well, you seem all right to me.

Queenie And to me. I think I've been put away because I
like a drink now and again. You see, sometimes,
after a drink, I forget where I am and I start
singing.

Bert What's wrong wi' that?

Queenie I don't know. But others objected. Bus conductors and people in the library. D'you know what you've been put away for?

Bert Yes. Me legs have gone.

Queenie Shame, you're a fine figure of a man.

Pause. She looks round.

Queenie I don't like it in here, do you? It's full of old people!

Bert I'm plannin' to escape.

Queenie What, dig a tunnel?

Bert No. I've got friends what are sortin' the paperwork out for me. It's only the paperwork what gets you out a' these places. Ay up there, Adrian! Ay up, Pandora!

Adrian 'Lo Bert.

Pandora kisses Bert.

Pandora How are you, darling?

Bert I'm not happy and that's the truth.

Adrian Cheer up, Bert. Russia's through to the European cup.

Bert cheers up.

Bert How's my Sabre?

Adrian He's outside in the garden. Matron said he could cause heart failure amongst the guests.

Bert I'm puttin' in an official complaint about *her*. Deprivin' a man of his liberty *and* his dog is unconstitutional.

Pandora speaks to Queenie:

Pandora Your hair is a lovely colour. What do you use?

Queenie I do it once a week with six ounces of red henna. It's a big slice out me pension but I'd sooner go without food than have white hair. I haven't got the personality to be an old age pensioner.

She speaks to Bert:

Queenie   Are you the only man in here?

Bert   Yes, I am.

Pandora   Women live longer than men. It's a sort of bonus
because we suffer more.

Queenie   I've hardly suffered at all. I've been happily
married three times. All dead now, of course.
But they died contented.

*Adrian and Pandora push Bert and Queenie in a
wheelchair gavotte, during:*

The Young Girl Inside You

Queenie   When you look in the mirror
The person reflected
Is a stranger you don't know
And don't care to meet:
But the young girl inside you
Is bright-eyed and flirty.
Not a day over thirty,
Who longs to be loved.

*Adrian and Pandora dance the gavotte behind
Bert and Queenie.*

Why does youth think it odd
That those older than God
Should know pangs of desire,
Feel the flame of love's fire?
It's not strange, it's not odd –
'Cause inside these old bodies
Our younger selves live
Just as lusty as you.

Wheelchair gavotte.

Queenie and Bert   Why does youth think it odd
That those older than God
Should know pangs of desire,
Feel the flame of love's fire?It's not strange, it's
not odd –
'Cause inside these old bodies

Our younger selves live
Just as lusty as you.

Queenie What am I doing in this thing?

She gets out of her wheelchair.

Pandora You've got something for Bert, haven't you, Adrian?

Bert Brought me some fags in, have you? Good lad.

He holds his hand out expectantly.

Adrian No, its a poem!

Bert is disappointed.

Bert Oh.

Queenie How lovely! Read it out then.

Adrian It's not very good.

Bert Don't bother then.

Pandora Darling, you're too modest – go on.

Adrian All right.

He reads the poem.

Adrian Poem to Bert – by Adrian Mole.

Bert, you are dead old.
Fond of Sabre, beetroot and Woodbines
We have nothing in common,
I am fourteen and a half,
You are eighty-nine
You smell, I don't.
Why we are friends
Is a mystery to me.

Bert is offended.

Queenie responds weakly:

Queenie Very nice, dear.

Bert It don't rhyme!

Adrian Would you mind if I sent your poem to the BBC, Bert?

Bert Yes, I would. they're all a load of drug addicts in the BBC. I've got it on good authority.

Queenie is impressed.

Queenie Oh, shocking! Know somebody high up, do you?

Bert Yes – a window cleaner at Broadcasting House.

Everybody laughs. Matron enters.

Matron Please! Your laughter is disturbing the other guests! Come along.

She claps her hands.

It's way past your bed time.

Pandora *Au contraire*, Matron! We can choose our own bed times.

Matron I was addressing myself to the oldsters, you cheeky young madam.

Adrian and Pandora leave.

Pandora and Adrian Bye, Bert. Bye, Queenie!

Bert and Queenie Bye!

Matron Time for bed.

Bert Bed? It's still light – I'm used to staying up till after the Epilogue.

Matron Here, we go to bed at half past nine.

Queenie We?

She looks coquettishly at Bert. Bert laughs dirtily. Queenie pushes Bert off.

Scene Eight

The Mole house. George is in the hall banging the telephone.

George Bloody British Telecom! Come on, get your act together! Give me a dialling tone.

He is getting increasingly enraged trying to get a line. He calls up to Adrian.

George Was there a storm in the night? Is the telephone pole still up?

Adrian calls down:

Adrian Oh no! Dad, I've got something to tell you!

George   Don't bother me now!

He speaks to the phone.

George   Come on. Come on! I want a job. I want some money in my pocket. I want to buy a round in the pub.

Adrian appears with the phone bills.

Adrian   Dad, we haven't paid the bill!

George   Because we haven't *had* the bill, you daft pillock!

Adrian   But *I* have Dad. I put it under my mattress.

George   Have you gone barmy? The bills go behind the clock. (*Pause.*) *When* did you put it under your mattress?

Adrian   Two months ago, Dad. We're not on the phone anymore!

George grabs the bill and reads it. He is stunned.

George   £287.37 pence.

He is amazed.

George   Operator calls: £231.00.

He shouts.

George   Who've you been phoning? The man in the bloody moon?

Adrian   No, Tunisia. Sorry Dad.

George replies weakly:

George   Sorry. He says he's sorry! He cuts me off from civilisation and he says he's sorry! I don't know why you don't finish me off completely, Adrian. Put rat poison in me tea. Come home one day and tell me you're pregnant. I give up. That's it. George Mole is no more. What you see is an empty shell.

George goes out (and offstage) through the kitchen. The dog barks off.

George   Not you an' all!

Scene Nine

Adrian opens a telegram.

Adrian A telegram! Addressed to me! The BBC? No –
from my mother. 'ADRIAN STOP COMING HOME
STOP.' What does she mean? 'Stop coming
home'? How can I stop coming home? I live
here!

*Adrian goes into the house and up to his room to
write his diary. Pauline enters on the side of the
stage. She is carrying her suitcases. She begins to
sing:*

Coming Down to Earth Again

Pauline Coming down to earth again
Out of sunshine into twilight:
Coming down to earth again
From my rocket flight.

Coming down to earth again
Terra Firma out of the sky:
Coming round on earth again –
Touch-down from on high.

I've had my fling: I let my hair right down,
I dreamed that I could survive without ties:
Dreaming was fine but now it's wake-up time
And I'm rubbing the sleep from my eyes.

Hello the life I thought I'd shed for good
And hello people I'd blocked from my mind:
After the wine at last it's own-up time
In the world I left behind.

Coming down to earth again,
I'm back home – coming in – coming home. . .

*Pauline goes upstairs and into the bedroom; she
and George kiss and hug.*

George Adrian! Your mother's home!

Adrian comes out of his room.

George Put the kettle on. We'll be down in a bit.

Adrian comes downstairs and speaks to the audience.

Adrian My mother threw herself on the mercy of my father. My father threw himself on the body of my mother. They've been in bed for two days – on and off. My mother told me why she left Rat-Fink Lucas. She said: 'Bimbo treated me like a sex object, Adrian, and he expected his evening meal cooked for him, and he cut his toe nails in the living-room! And, besides, I'm very fond of your father … ' She didn't mention me! My only hope for future happiness now rests with the BBC. If they would give me my own poetry programme on Radio Four I would have an outlet for the intellectual side of my nature. I haven't got enough emotions to cope with the complexities of my everyday life. I rang Pandora and told her that my mother had come back and she came round after her viola lesson. I'm glad I've got her. Love is the only thing that keeps me sane. Goodnight.

This is the end of the play, although the curtain call is done at Bert and Queenie's wedding. The cast wear their best clothes and flowers in their buttonholes. When Bert and Queenie take their call they are showered with confetti and rice. Mr Lucas prepares to take the wedding photograph. Adrian enters last – just in time to be in the photograph.

Questions and Explorations

1 Keeping Track

These questions are here to make you stop and think more carefully about what's happening in the play.

Act One

1 New Year's Eve party

'Honestly, Adrian, your consumer durables are a disgrace.' (p 3)

What does Nigel mean by this?

2 The Mole living room

George is moaning about the cost of electricity. On the one hand he says '. . .until you . . .start bringing some money into this house, I shall be as obsessive as I like.' The next thing he says is 'No wife of mine goes out to work!' (p8)

What do you think he really wants? How does this make Pauline feel?

3 School playground

a) Why does Pandora like to be called Box?

b) What is the difference between 'clever' and 'intellectual'? (A dictionary will help here.) Which one would you rather be and why?

4 Bert Baxter's house

'Don't smoke! A lad of your age! You should be ashamed of yourself!' (p 21)

Is much pressure like this put on young people to smoke? Why do so many teenagers smoke?

5 Bully scene

Did you find yourself laughing during this scene? But is bullying funny? Why does Sue Townsend make this a humorous scene?

6 Paper round

Pandora's family have *The Guardian, Private Eye, Punch* and *New Society* delivered. What is this supposed to tell us about this family?

7 Assertiveness training

a) Pauline has gone to a workshop on assertiveness training for women. What is 'assertiveness' training? Why does she feel she needs it?

b) The result is that Adrian and his father have to do more housework. Look at the list of things Adrian has had to do. (p 29). Is this fair? Who had to do them before?

8 The Moles' kitchen

'We're like two sunbeams dancing on the ceiling of life.'

Why does Mr Lucas talk in this way to Pauline? Find other examples of him using this 'flowery' language.

9 The Moles' garden

Read through the argument in the garden scene again. If you

had to think of a good, catchy headline for a newspaper report on the event what would it be?

Act Two

1 Bert's house

Bert tells Adrian that his Bible saved his life during the war, but it was printed in 1958. How do you know he must be lying? Why do you think he lies to Adrian?

2 The Moles' living-room

a) George buys flowers for Pauline, but takes them round to Doreen Slater when Pauline leaves. What does this tell you about George?

b) Later, Adrian's grandma manages to sort out the bullying problem. We are given no clues as to how she manages this. Try to imagine what might have happened.

3 School

a) Why does Adrian wear red socks to school? Is there anything about your school rules that you would like to change? If so, what and why?

b) Adrian says that it's sexist just to like Pandora for her looks. Do you agree? Is this a bad thing?

c) Pandora wants to change our 'spiritually bankrupt society'. What does she mean by this, and do you agree that society needs changing?

4 Alderman Cooper Sunshine Home

a) Do you think that the old people are treated fairly at the home? If you could change anything about it, what would it be?

b) Adrian writes a poem for Bert (p 75), just as he wrote one for Pandora earlier (p70). What do you think of his poetry?

2 Explorations

A Life as a teenager

'Perhaps when my diary is discovered people will understand the torment of being a thirteen-and-three-quarter-year old intellectual.' *(p 1)*

The diary that Adrian keeps is one way in which he copes with the events that take place in his life. He is under a great deal of pressure to conform to what is expected of a teenager. His clothes need to be right; Nigel criticises him for looking like Frank Bough:

'Go and stand in the corner. I'm ashamed to be seen with you. Don't you care what you look like?' *(p 19)*

1 Discuss, in groups, what is expected of you as a teenager (your behaviour, attitude, clothes etc.)

by a) teachers

   b) parents

   c) friends.

2 Then discuss:

a) Whether girls responded differently to boys. If so why?

b) What happens when people's expectations of your behaviour varies, eg when your parents expect one thing from you and your friends another?

B Teenagers and the media

'But Adrian's not a normal teenager, George.' 'Yes, I am!' 'Don't be silly, of course you're not. You're polite to me and your dad, and you keep your room tidy and you don't play your stereo system at full decibels.' (p 7)

1 How are teenagers portrayed in the media? Think about TV programmes aimed directly at a teenage audience. Look through magazines and newspapers. Make a collage of images.

2 Think about the issues and problems that concern teenagers. Choose one and write a letter about it to a 'problem page'.

3 Swap letters with a partner and write replies to each other's letter. Think about it carefully, then give the most helpful, reassuring advice you can.

4 Create your own magazine for teenagers. Don't just base it on what's available in the shops already; they are created by adults. Now's your chance to produce something that you really think you and your friends would buy.

C Old Age

1 When you hear the words 'pensioner' and 'old age' what do you instantly think of? Quickly jot down as many images and ideas as you can.

2 Now think about the old people in the play, Bert Baxter, Queenie and Adrian's grandma.

'Queenie: I haven't the personality to be an old age pensioner.'
(p 73)

Make notes on these characters (the things they say, the things they do) and draw a sketch of how you imagine they look. Do these three characters fit in to your original ideas about old people?

3 Now read this poem:

When I am an old woman I shall wear purple
With a red hat which doesn't go, and doesn't suit me,
And I shall spend my pension on brandy and summer gloves
and satin sandals, and say we've no money for butter.
I shall sit down on the pavement when I'm tired
And gobble up samples in shops and press alarm bells
And run my stick along the public railings
And make up for the sobriety of my youth.
I shall go out in my slippers in the rain
And pick the flowers in other peoples' gardens
And learn to spit.
You can wear terrible shirts and grow more fat
And eat three pounds of sausages at a go
Or only bread and pickle for a week
and hoard pens and pencils and beermats and things in boxes.
But now we must have clothes that keep us dry
and pay our rent and not swear in the street

And set a good example for the children
We will have friends to dinner and read the papers.
But maybe I ought to practise a little now?
So people who know me are not too shocked and surprised
When suddenly I am old, and start to wear purple.
Jenny Joseph

(From *Rose in the Afternoon*, J M Dent 1974)

a) There are plenty of unexpected things she would like to do. Do any of them appeal to you?

b) Has it ever occurred to you that someone old would have these desires?

c) Now, using the woman in the poem, and the three older characters in the play for ideas, create your own character, who happens to be a pensioner. Use him or her in a story, play or poem.

D Bullying

Barry Kent makes Adrian give him 25p a day 'menaces' money. While it is easy to laugh at Barry, particularly when he sings 'Sorry gotta do it', bullying is, in fact, no joke.

1 Make a list of reasons why Adrian is bullied. Now add to this, with any other reasons why people are bullied.

2 So, why is it that some people do the bullying? Make a new list, trying to think of as many reasons as possible.

3 Because bullying is very common, many stories have been written about it – see if you can find any in school. Write your own story called 'The Bully'. You could either be the bully or

the victim. Try to really let the reader know what it feels like to be in your situation.

4 Now role play. Work on a piece of drama based on a bullying incident. Think about:

– Why is it that the bully bullies?

– How is the situation 'worked out' in the end?

5 What advice would you give to someone who is being bullied? Design a poster giving this advice, perhaps for younger pupils at your school.

E Humour

Many of the events that occur in *Adrian Mole* are of a serious nature; Adrian being bullied, his parents' separation. Finding it difficult to 'fit in' with other teenagers etc., yet these events are treated in a humorous way; the play is a funny one.

1 Do you think that this is a good thing, or do you think that serious events should be treated in a serious way?

2 Can you think of any reasons why Sue Townsend chose to use humour?

3 Have a go at looking at a relatively serious issue/event in a more light-hearted way. (Remember though, to do this sensitively and thoughtfully; the last thing you want to do is upset people!)

Music for the Play

Overture: The Mole Theme

The Mole Theme

This forms a part of the overture
and is also used between a number of scenes,
in varying musical styles, throughout the show
and as a background to the house-cleaning scene (page 29),
starting slowly and getting faster.

The House Where I Live

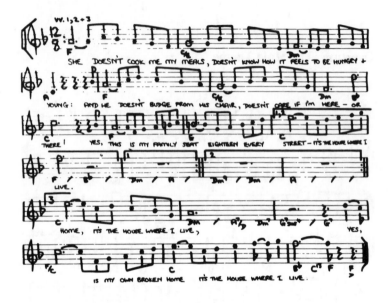

Sorry, Gotta Do It

The Bad Old Days

Your Hair of Gold

Family Trio

Your Dead Grandad

Get It Right!

Dog

YOU ARE MY ONLY TRUE FRIEND, ALWAYS HERE AT THE END OF A TRAUMATIC DAY: I'M USED TO YOUR SLOBB'RING EMBRACE + YOUR LOP-SIDED FACE ... IS O. K OH DOG. NEVER GAVE YOU A NAME, STILL I'M GLAD THAT YOU CAME TO THE HOUSE WHERE I LIVE STORM IN THE HOUSE WHERE WE LIVE.

The Other Woman

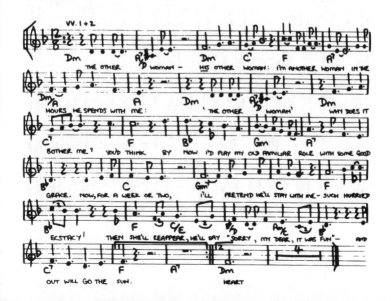

THE OTHER WOMAN — HIS OTHER WOMAN: I'M ANOTHER WOMAN IN THE HOURS HE SPENDS WITH ME: 'THE OTHER WOMAN' WHY DOES IT BOTHER ME? YOU'D THINK BY NOW I'D PLAY MY OLD FAMILIAR ROLE WITH SOME GOOD GRACE. NOW, FOR A WEEK OR TWO, I'LL PRETEND HE'LL STAY WITH ME— SUCH HURRIED ECSTACY! THEN SHE'LL REAPPEAR, HE'LL SAY "SORRY, MY DEAR, IT WAS FUN"— AND OUT WILL GO THE SUN. HEART

Oh, Pandora

The Young Girl Inside You

Coming Down to Earth Again

Bibliography

Other works by Sue Townsend

Plays:

Womberang Methuen (Soho Poly, London, 1979)

Dayroom (Croydon Warehouse, 1981)

The Ghost of Daniel Lambert (Leicester Phoenix, 1981)

Bazaar & Rummage Methuen (Royal Court, Theatre Upstairs, London, 1982, BBC Television, 1983)

Groping for Words Methuen (Croydon Warehouse, 1983)

The Great Celestial Cow Methuen (Joint Stock on tour and at the Royal Court, 1984)

Ear, Nose and Throat (touring, 1988)

Ten Tiny Fingers, Nine Tiny Toes Methuen (Library Theatre, Manchester, 1989).

Fiction:

The Secret Diary of Adrian Mole Aged 13 $\frac{3}{4}$ Methuen, 1983

The Growing Pains of Adrian Mole Methuen, 1985

Rebuilding Coventry Methuen, 1988

The Secret Diary of Adrian Mole Song Book (in collaboration with Ken Howard and Alan Blaikley) Methuen, 1985

True Confessions of Adrian Albert Mole Margaret Hilda Roberts and Susan Lilian Townsend Methuen, 1989

Glossary

Act 1

Page

1	*George Elliot*	The pen name of a nineteenth-century female writer called Mary Ann Evans
8	*obsessive*	being completely preoccupied with something (in this case, money)
8	*The Female Enuch*	an early feminist book, written by Germaine Greer
10	*lurex*	a stretchy, glittery material
16	*juvenile*	childish
22	*The Morning Star*	newspaper of communist party
33	*Lenin*	a leader of the Russian Revolution, 1917

Act 2

43	*Ypres*	the site of a First World War battle in France
50	*Barbara Cartland*	writer of romantic fiction
65	*revolution*	the overthrow of society by the ordinary people in that society
65	*revisionism*	going back on your original ideas
65	*oppression*	to suffer harsh, authoritarian rule
66	*philistine*	one who does not appreciate aesthetic values (eg good plays, fine art, etc.)

Children's Ward

Age 12+

Paul Abbott, John Chambers and Kay Mellor
Granada TV

Six scripts from the popular Granada TV series Children's
Ward. The plays trace the fortunes of patients admitted to
the children's ward and the relationships between them.

   Children's Ward also examines the way the programmes
are made, and is an excellent medium for discussing the
nature of television drama.

ISBN: 435 23285 1

Whale   **Age 10+**

David Holman

Whale is based on the real events of October 1988 when
three Californian grey whales became trapped under the
Arctic ice-cap in Alaska. The play captures the suspense of
the rescue and sees the incident through the eyes of both
adults and the children who supported the campaign.

  Whale offers many discussion possibilities on green
issues, the role of the media and Inuit culture and way of
life. The introduction and notes supply ideas, background
information and activities for using these opportunities to
the full.

ISBN: 435 23286 X

The Play of The Monster Garden   Age 10+

Diane Samuels

Based on the popular novel by Vivien Alcock, this tells the story of Frankie, daughter of the genetic scientist Professor Stein, and the unexpected results she gets when she cultivates 'jelly' taken from his laboratory. The resulting tale is both funny and thoughtful, raising issues surrounding experimentation, the treatment of living creatures and the nature of friendship.

ISBN: 435 23284 3
(The novel of *The Monster Garden* is also available in New Windmills)